PRENTICE HALL

Realidades Ⓑ

Practice Workbook with Writing, Audio & Video Activities

with FCAT Support

Shawn Eric Denight

Jan Lemus, M.Ed.

PEARSON

Prentice Hall

Boston, Massachusetts
Upper Saddle River, New Jersey

Pearson Prentice Hall™ is a trademark of Pearson Education, Inc.
Pearson® is a registered trademark of Pearson plc.
Prentice Hall® is a registered trademark of Pearson Education, Inc.

ISBN 0-13-166039-X

3 4 5 6 7 8 9 10   V004   11

Practice Workbook

Realidades Ⓑ

Capítulo 5A

Nombre _____

Fecha _____

Hora _____

Practice Workbook **5A–1**

La familia

A. Patricia is telling you about her family. Label each person in her family tree with a word that describes his or her relationship to Patricia. You may use some words more than once.

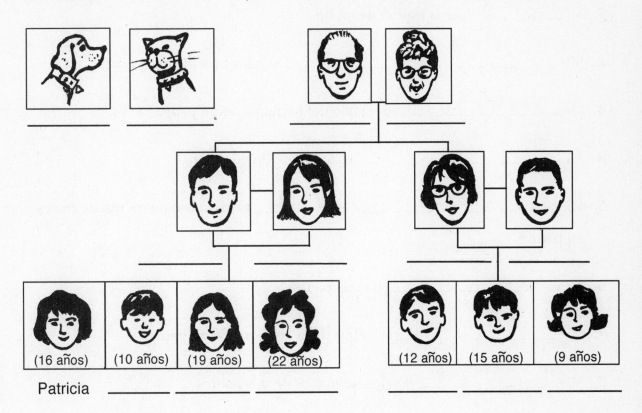

_____ _____   _____

_____

_____ _____

(16 años)   (10 años)   (19 años)   (22 años)   (12 años)   (15 años)   (9 años)

Patricia _____ _____ _____   _____ _____ _____

B. Now, answer the following questions by circling **sí** or **no**.

1. ¿Patricia tiene hermanastros?   Sí   No

2. ¿Patricia tiene hermanas mayores?   Sí   No

3. ¿Patricia tiene dieciséis años?   Sí   No

4. ¿Patricia tiene tres primos menores?   Sí   No

5. ¿Patricia tiene dos abuelas?   Sí   No

¿Quién es?

A. Complete the sentences below with the correct family relationships.

1. Mi ___ ___ ◯___ es la esposa de mi tío.

2. Mis ___ ___ ___ ◯___ ___ ___ ___ ___ son los hijos de mis padres.

3. Mi ___ ___ ◯___ ___ es el hijo del hermano de mi padre.

4. Mi ◯___ ___ ___ ___ ___ es la madre de mi madre.

5. Mi ___ ___ ___ ___ ___ ___ ◯___ es el esposo de mi madre (no es mi padre).

6. Yo soy la ___ ___ ___ ◯ de mis padres.

7. Mi ___ ___ ◯___ es la hija de la hermana de mi padre.

8. Mis ◯___ ___ ___ son los hermanos de mis padres.

9. Mamá y papá son mis ___ ___ ◯___ ___ ___ .

10. Mis ___ ___ ◯___ ___ ___ ___ ◯___ ___ ___ ___ son las hijas de la esposa de mi padre (no son mis hermanas).

B. Now, unscramble the circled letters to come up with another member of the family.

___ ___ ___ ___ ___ ___ ___ ___ ___ ___ ___

Go Online WEB CODE jcd-0501
PHSchool.com

Realidades B

Capítulo 5A

Nombre _____

Hora _____

Fecha _____

Practice Workbook **5A–3**

¡Una fiesta inesperada (*a surprise party*)!

The Rodríguez family is giving their older son Tomás a surprise birthday party. Complete their conversation, using the most logical word from the word bank.

luces	la piñata	tiene	decoraciones
dulces	pastel	celebrar	sólo
globos	sacar fotos	regalos	

MAMÁ: Vamos a hacer el plan porque vamos a _____ el cumpleaños

de Tomás. Él _____ doce años.

TÍA LULÚ: Sí, ¡vamos a celebrar! Primero, necesitamos un _____ para

comer ¿no? ¡Qué sabroso!

MAMÁ: Sí. Y necesitamos unas _____ perfectas. Vamos a necesitar un

globo y una luz.

TÍA LULÚ: ¿ _____ *un* globo y *una* luz? ¡No, necesitamos muchos

_____ y muchas _____! También

necesitamos papel picado.

PABLITO: Oye, ¡yo tengo una cámara fabulosa! Puedo _____ en la fiesta

cuando Tomás abre los _____ .

MAMÁ: Sí, Pablito. ¡Muchas gracias! Y finalmente, pueden romper

_____ . ¿Tenemos _____?

TÍA LULÚ: Sí, tenemos muchos dulces.

PABLITO: ¡Qué buena fiesta!

Realidades B

Capítulo 5A

Nombre _____

Hora _____

Fecha _____

Practice Workbook **5A–4**

La celebración

Raúl is explaining how he and his family are preparing for his sister's birthday party. Read his description and answer the questions that follow in complete sentences.

> Hoy es el cumpleaños de mi hermana menor, Gabriela. Mis padres y yo preparamos la fiesta. Mi mamá decora con el papel picado y las luces. Mi papá tiene los regalos y los globos. Yo preparo la mesa con los globos y el pastel. También tengo la cámara porque voy a hacer un video de la fiesta.
>
> Sólo nuestra familia va a estar aquí, pero con todos mis primos, mis tíos y mis abuelos tenemos muchas personas. A las cinco mi hermana va a estar aquí y la fiesta va a empezar.

1. ¿Quién es Gabriela? _____

2. ¿Para quién es la fiesta? _____

3. ¿Qué clase de fiesta es? _____

4. ¿Con qué decora Raúl? _____

5. ¿Qué tiene el papá? _____

6. ¿Qué va a hacer Raúl? _____

7. ¿Quiénes van a estar en la fiesta? _____

_____

8. ¿A qué hora va a empezar la fiesta? _____

Go Online WEB CODE jcd-0502
PHSchool.com

Realidades Ⓑ

Capítulo 5A

Nombre _____

Fecha _____

Hora _____

Practice Workbook **5A–5**

Conversaciones

You overhear a group of students talking. Fill in the blanks in their conversations with the correct forms of the verb **tener**.

1. FRANCO: Hola, Carmen. ¿Qué tienes en la mano?

   CARMEN: (Yo) _____ un regalo para mi primo. Es su cumpleaños.

   FRANCO: Ah, ¿sí? ¿Cuántos años _____?

   CARMEN: _____ doce años.

   FRANCO: Mis primos también _____ doce años.

2. ELENA: ¡Oye, Carlos! ¿Cuántos años _____?

   CARLOS: ¿Yo? Yo _____ quince años. ¿Por qué?

   ELENA: Porque mi hermano y yo _____ una prima de quince

   años que _____ que ir a un baile el viernes. ¿(Tú)

   _____ planes?

   CARLOS: ¿El viernes? No, no _____ otros planes.

3. PABLO: Hola, José. Hola, Manolo. ¿(Uds.) _____ un dólar?

   JOSÉ: Sí, yo _____ un dólar. ¿Por qué?

   PABLO: Porque yo _____ hambre y quiero comprar un perrito

   caliente.

   MANOLO: ¿La cafetería _____ perritos calientes buenos?

   PABLO: Sí. ¿Quieres uno?

   JOSÉ: Sí, pero primero Manolo y yo _____ que ir a clase.

   PABLO: También _____ que ir a clase.

Realidades B

Capítulo 5A

Nombre _____

Hora _____

Fecha _____

Practice Workbook **5A–6**

¿De quién es?

A. Fill in the following chart with the masculine and feminine, singular and plural forms of the possessive adjectives indicated.

hijo	tía	abuelos	hermanas
			mis hermanas
	tu tía		
su hijo			
		nuestros abuelos	
vuestro hijo	vuestra tía	vuestros abuelos	vuestras hermanas

B. Now, complete the following sentences by writing in the possessive adjective that corresponds with the English adjective in parentheses. Follow the model.

Modelo (my) ___Mi___ abuela es vieja.

1. (our) _____ abuelos van a la casa para hablar con nosotros.

2. (your) Sara, gracias por _____ libro.

3. (my) _____ prima es de Tejas.

4. (your) ¿Tienen mucha tarea en _____ clase de matemáticas?

5. (their) _____ tíos están en la oficina ahora.

6. (my) El perro come _____ galletas.

7. (our) Nosotros vamos a la escuela en _____ bicicletas.

8. (your) Profesor, ¿dónde está _____ oficina?

9. (their) _____ hijo es muy trabajador.

10. (his) _____ hermana está enferma.

Go Online WEB CODE jcd-0505 PHSchool.com

Los regalos perfectos

Using the subjects below and the activities suggested by the pictures, write complete sentences about what your friends and relatives have for the party. Make sure you use the correct possessive adjective. Follow the model.

Mi primo Juan

Modelo *Mi primo Juan tiene su cámara.*

Mis tíos

1. _____

Alicia

2. _____

Tú

3. _____

Nosotros

4. _____

Yo

5. _____

Ud.

6. _____

La profesora Méndez

7. _____

Nosotras

8. _____

Realidades Ⓑ

Capítulo 5A

Nombre _____

Hora _____

Fecha _____

Practice Workbook **5A–8**

Repaso

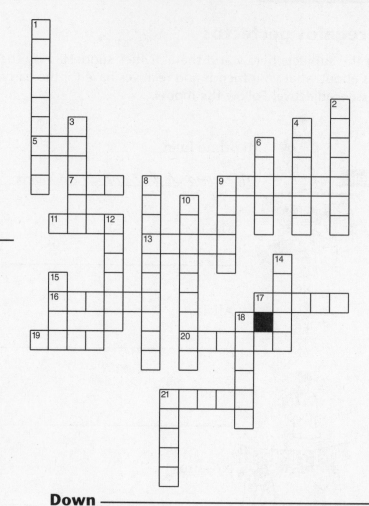

Across

5. La madre de mi primo es mi ____.

7. El hermano de mi padre es mi ____.

9. *sister*

11.

13. mi papá; el ____

16. La mamá de mi padre es mi ____.

17. Mi hermano y yo somos los ____ de nuestros padres.

19.

20.

21. mi mamá; la ____

Down

1. El esposo de mi madre; no es mi papá, es mi ____.

2. *brother*

3.

4. el papel ____

6.

8. ¡Feliz ____! ¿Cuántos años tienes?

9. Quiero ____ un video.

10. la madre de mi hermanastro; mi ____

12. Los hijos ____ la piñata.

14. Es el hermano de mi prima; mi ____.

15. ¿Quién ____ las fotos de la fiesta?

18. *parents*

21. no menor

Realidades B

Capítulo 5A

Nombre _____

Fecha _____

Hora _____

Practice Workbook **5A–9**

Organizer

I. Vocabulary

To describe family relationships

_____

_____

_____

_____

_____

_____

_____

Activities at a party

_____

_____

_____

Items at a party

_____

_____

_____

_____

Words to express possession

_____

_____

_____

_____

II. Grammar

1. The forms of **tener** are: _____ _____

_____ _____

_____ _____

2. Possessive adjectives in Spanish are written as follows:

	Singular/Plural		Singular/Plural
my	_____ / _____	our	_____ / _____
your (familiar)	_____ / _____	your (pl., familiar)	_____ / _____
your (formal), his, hers	_____ / _____	your (pl., formal), their	_____ / _____

Restaurante elegante

Label the following items with the correct word. Don't forget to use the correct definite article (**el** or **la**).

1. _____   5. _____   9. _____

2. _____   6. _____   10. _____

3. _____   7. _____   11. _____

4. _____   8. _____

Go Online WEB CODE jcd-0511
PHSchool.com

Las descripciones

You are telling your friends about some of your family members. Write descriptions of them in complete sentences. Follow the model.

Paco

Modelo _Paco es alto y tiene el pelo corto y negro._

El tío Roberto

1. _____
_____
_____

Melinda, mi madrastra

2. _____
_____
_____

El abuelito Jorge

3. _____
_____
_____

Los primos Juan y Manuel

4. _____
_____
_____

Esperanza

5. _____
_____
_____

La palabra correcta

Complete the following mini-conversations with the most logical words or phrases from your vocabulary.

1. —¿Necesita Ud. algo?

   —Sí, me _____ un tenedor.

2. —¿Te gusta la comida del Sr. Vargas?

   —Sí, es deliciosa. ¡Qué _____!

3. —¿Quieres otra _____ de café?

   —No, gracias.

4. —¿Desea Ud. un té helado?

   —Sí, porque tengo _____.

5. —¿Qué vas a _____ de postre?

   —Yo quiero el flan.

6. —¿Necesitan _____ más?

   —Sí, la cuenta por favor.

7. —Muchas gracias.

   —De _____.

8. —¿Qué quisiera Ud. de _____ _____?

   —Me gustaría el arroz con pollo.

9. —¿Estás cansado?

   —Sí, tengo _____.

10. —¿Bebes el café?

    —Sí, porque tengo _____.

Go Online WEB CODE jcd-0512
PHSchool.com

Cita (*date*) en español

A. David and Rocío are on a date at a Spanish restaurant. Using the vocabulary you have learned in this chapter, write their possible responses to the waiter's questions. Use complete sentences.

CAMARERO: ¿Qué desean Uds. de plato principal?

DAVID: _____

ROCÍO: _____

CAMARERO: ¿Cómo está la comida?

DAVID: _____

ROCÍO: _____

CAMARERO: ¿Desean algo más?

DAVID: _____

ROCÍO: _____

B. Now, based on the waiter's responses, write what you think David or Rocío may have asked the waiter.

DAVID: ¿_____?

CAMARERO: Sí, le traigo una servilleta.

ROCÍO: ¿_____?

CAMARERO: Sí, ahora puede pedir algo de postre.

DAVID: ¿_____?

CAMARERO: Un café, por supuesto. ¿Tiene sueño?

Realidades B

Capítulo 5B

Nombre _____

Fecha _____

Hora _____

Practice Workbook **5B–5**

¿Quién viene?

Your class has decided to put on a talent show, and you are in charge of scheduling what time everyone is coming to audition for different skits. Your friend Lola is anxious to know the schedule. Answer her questions using the picture below. Follow the model.

Modelo   ¿Quién viene a las ocho y media?
   La Sra. Ramos viene a las ocho y media.

1. ¿Quién viene a las nueve?

   _____

2. ¿Quién viene a las diez?

   _____

3. ¿Quién viene a las once menos cuarto?

   _____

4. ¿Quién viene a las once y media?

   _____

5. ¿Quién viene a las doce?

   _____

6. ¿Quién viene a la una?

   _____

7. ¿Quién viene a las dos y media?

   _____

8. ¿Quién viene a las tres y media?

   _____

Go Online WEB CODE jcd-0513
PHSchool.com

Una carta para mamá

Read the following letter from Rosaura to her mom in Spain. Write the form of **ser** or **estar** that best completes each sentence.

Querida mamá:

¡Aquí _____ en Chicago! Chicago _____ una gran ciudad

con muchas personas que _____ muy interesantes. La comida

_____ fantástica. La especialidad _____ la pizza. ¡Qué rica!

Vivo con una familia muy simpática. Tienen un hijo que siempre

_____ contento y una hija que _____ muy estudiosa.

¡_____ las nueve de la noche y ella _____ en la biblioteca!

Los chicos de la escuela también _____ estudiosos, pero no muy

serios. Mis compañeros y yo _____ muy buenos amigos y

_____ juntos todos los fines de semana. Una amiga, Vera,

_____ boliviana y _____ divertidísima. Vera y yo

_____ en la misma clase de biología.

Bueno, mamá, _____ muy tarde. Mañana voy a _____

muy ocupada y necesito dormir. Pero sabes ahora que todo _____

bien aquí y que yo _____ contenta. Besos para ti y para papá.

Un abrazo,

Rosaura

Realidades B

Capítulo 5B

Nombre _____

Hora _____

Fecha _____

Practice Workbook **5B–7**

¿Qué van a comer?

The Vázquez family is getting ready to order dinner in a restaurant. Look at the pictures to get an idea of the person's needs. Answer the questions below using vocabulary that would most logically go in each situation.

1.

¿Cómo está la Sra. Vázquez? _____

¿Qué debe pedir de plato principal? _____

¿De postre? _____ ¿Y para beber? _____

2.

¿Cómo están los chicos? _____

¿Qué deben pedir de plato principal? _____

¿De postre? _____ ¿Y para beber? _____

3.

¿Cómo está Elisita? _____

¿Qué debe pedir de plato principal? _____

¿De postre? _____ ¿Y para beber? _____

4.

¿Cómo está el Sr. Vázquez? _____

¿Qué debe pedir de plato principal? _____

¿De postre? _____ ¿Y para beber? _____

Go Online WEB CODE jcd-0515
PHSchool.com

Realidades B

Capítulo 5B

Nombre _____

Hora _____

Fecha _____

Practice Workbook **5B–8**

Repaso

Across

6. *blond;* el pelo ____

7. No bajo ____ .

8. Uds. ____ cansados.

12. Paquito no es viejo. Es ____ .

13. ¡Camarero, la ____ por favor!

15.

16. Mi abuela tiene el pelo ____ .

17. Ella tiene 88 años. Es ____ .

18. Necesito un cuchillo y un ____ para comer el bistec.

19. sal y ____

21. Necesito un té. Tengo ____ .

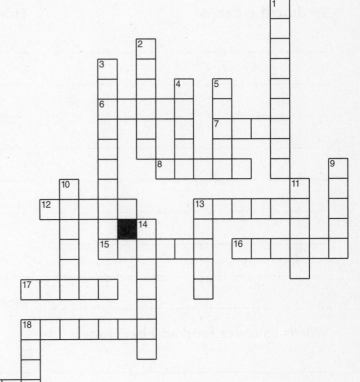

Down

1. *red-haired (m.)*

2. El Sr. López es un ____ .

3. *napkin*

4. Nosotros ____ bajos.

5. *good-looking (f.)*

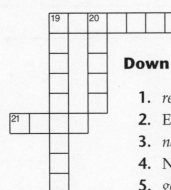

9. ____ el pelo ____

10. ¿Qué quieres de ____? El flan.

11. Quiero un té helado. Tengo ____ .

13. no largo

14.

18. Quiero una ____ de café.

19. el plato ____

20. La Sra. Miranda es una ____ .

Realidades B

Capítulo 5B

Nombre _____

Hora _____

Fecha _____

Practice Workbook **5B–9**

Organizer

I. Vocabulary

To describe people

_____

_____

_____

_____

_____

_____

_____

_____

Words to order food and beverages

_____

_____

_____

_____

Things at a restaurant

_____

_____

_____

_____

_____

Words to describe how you're feeling

_____

_____

_____

II. Grammar

1. The forms of **venir** are: _____ _____

   _____ _____

   _____ _____

2. For physical and personality descriptions, and to tell what time it is, use the verb

   _____. To talk about location and physical and emotional states,

   use the verb _____.

WEB CODE jcd-0516
PHSchool.com

Realidades B

Capítulo 6A

Nombre _____

Fecha _____

Hora _____

Practice Workbook **6A–1**

Un dormitorio nuevo para mí

Ignacio is moving into his sister's room when she goes away to college. His parents have told him that he can bring anything into his new room that he can carry by himself. Make a list of eight things that he would definitely be able to bring with him, and five things that he definitely wouldn't be able to bring. Use the examples given to help you.

Traer conmigo

_____ *El lector DVD*

_____

_____

_____

_____

_____

_____

_____

No traer conmigo

_____ *La pared*

_____

_____

_____

_____

Muchos colores

Write the names of the color or colors that you associate with the following things. Don't forget to make the colors agree in gender and number.

1. el jugo de naranja _____.

2. la limonada _____.

3. el 14 de febrero _____.

4. el 25 de diciembre _____.

5. el sol _____.

6. la nieve _____.

7. unas zanahorias _____.

8. la bandera de los Estados Unidos _____.

9. un tomate _____.

10. la piscina _____.

11. la noche _____.

12. el Día de San Patricio _____.

Go Online WEB CODE jcd-0601
PHSchool.com

La experiencia nueva

A. Read the letter that Gloria wrote to her friend in Spain about her host family in Chile.

> Querida Sandra,
>
> Lo paso muy bien aquí con la familia Quijano. Desde el primer día aquí, tengo mi propio dormitorio. Hay una cama, una mesita, una lámpara, un escritorio con una silla pequeña y un espejo. También hay una ventana con cortinas amarillas. La mejor cosa del cuarto es la lámpara. Es roja, negra y marrón y es muy artística. Creo que es la lámpara más bonita del mundo.
>
> El cuarto también es bonito. Las paredes son moradas. Sólo quiero mi equipo de sonido y mis discos compactos.
>
> Abrazos,
>
> *Gloria*

B. Now, answer these questions in complete sentences.

1. ¿A Gloria le gusta la familia?

   _____

2. ¿Comparte Gloria el dormitorio con otro estudiante?

   _____

3. ¿De qué color son las paredes en el dormitorio de Gloria?

   _____

4. ¿Tiene Gloria su equipo de sonido en su dormitorio?

   _____

5. ¿Cómo es la lámpara en el dormitorio de Gloria? ¿A ella le gusta?

   _____

6. ¿De qué color son las cortinas en el dormitorio de Gloria?

   _____

¿Dónde está todo?

Movers just finished putting everything into Marcela's new room. Help her locate everything by describing where the items are in the picture below. Follow the model.

Modelo _Una lámpara está al lado del televisor._

_____

_____

_____

_____

_____

_____

_____

Go Online WEB CODE jcd-0602
PHSchool.com

Realidades **B**

Capítulo 6A

Nombre _____

Fecha _____

Hora _____

Practice Workbook **6A–5**

Las comparaciones

Felipe and Mónica are brother and sister who are very different from each other. Using their pictures and the model to help you, write comparisons of the two siblings. Remember to make the adjectives agree in gender with the subject.

Modelo Mónica / alto *Mónica es más alta que Felipe.* _____

1. Felipe / serio _____

2. Mónica / sociable _____

3. Mónica / rubio _____

4. Felipe / estudioso _____

5. Felipe / alto _____

6. Mónica / viejo _____

7. Felipe / rubio _____

8. Felipe / joven _____

9. Mónica / serio _____

Los premios Óscar

The following chart rates movies according to certain categories. Four stars is the best rating, one star is the worst rating. Using the chart as a guide, write complete sentences comparing the three movies. Follow the model.

	Una tarde en agosto	*Mi vida*	*Siete meses en Lima*
Actores – talentosos	****	**	***
Fotografía – artística	****	*	***
Ropa – bonita	***	****	***
Director – creativo	****	***	**
Cuento – interesante	****	**	*

Modelo actores / "Una tarde en agosto"

Los actores de "Una tarde en agosto" son los más talentosos.

1. fotografía / "Una tarde en agosto"

   _____

2. fotografía / "Mi vida"

   _____

3. director / "Una tarde en agosto"

   _____

4. actores / "Una tarde en agosto"

   _____

5. director / "Siete meses en Lima"

   _____

6. ropa / "Mi vida"

   _____

7. cuento / "Siete meses en Lima"

   _____

8. actores / "Mi vida"

   _____

9. cuento / "Una tarde en agosto"

   _____

Go Online WEB CODE jcd-0604
PHSchool.com

Realidades B

Capítulo 6A

Nombre _____

Hora _____

Fecha _____

Practice Workbook **6A–7**

Las mini-conversaciones

A. Fill in the rest of these conjugations.

	DORMIR	PODER
yo		
tú		*puedes*
él, ella, Ud.	*duerme*	
nosotros		
vosotros	*dormís*	*podéis*
ellos, ellas, Uds.		

B. Write the correct forms of either **dormir** or **poder** in the blanks to complete the mini-conversations below.

1. —¿Quieres ir al cine?

   —No _____. Tengo que trabajar.

2. —¿Cuántas horas _____ cada noche?

   —Generalmente ocho horas.

3. —¿Uds. _____ venir a nuestra fiesta?

   —Sí. ¿A qué hora es?

4. —Nosotros no _____ trabajar hoy.

   —Está bien. Van a trabajar mañana.

5. —Cuando ellas van de cámping, ¿dónde _____?

   —Pues, en sus camas Coleman, por supuesto.

6. —¿Qué haces a las once y media de la noche?

   —¡Yo _____!

7. —¿_____ (tú) hablar con tu abuela por teléfono?

   —No, no _____ porque estoy ocupado.

8. —¿Qué hace una chica cansada?

   —_____ mucho.

Realidades **B**

Capítulo 6A

Nombre

Hora

Fecha

Practice Workbook **6A-8**

Repaso

Down

1. Tengo que ___ por la noche.

2.
3. el ___ DVD
4. no pequeño

5.
6. un ___ compacto
8. no es a la derecha; es a la ___
11. Un plátano es de color ___.
13. *dresser*
17. La nieve es de color ___.
18. no mejor

Across

2. Rojo y azul son ___.

7.

9.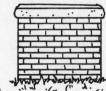

10. el ___ de sonido
11. Hay una ___ debajo de la cama.
12. Uds. tienen mucha ropa en el ___.
14. Los libros están en el ___.
15. *brown*
16. no es fea, es ___
19. Duermo en la ___.
20. *mirror*

Realidades Ⓑ

Capítulo 6A

Nombre _____

Hora _____

Fecha _____

Practice Workbook **6A–9**

Organizer

I. Vocabulary

To talk about things in a bedroom

_____

_____

_____

_____

_____

_____

_____

Electronic equipment

_____

_____

_____

_____

_____

Words to talk about colors

_____

_____

_____

_____

Words to describe things

_____

_____

_____

_____

II. Grammar

1. To compare peoples' ages, use either _____ + **que** or _____ + **que**. To say that something is "better than" use _____ + **que**; to say that something is "worse than" use _____ + **que**.

2. To say that something is the "best" or "worst" use the following construction: article + _____ / _____ + noun. To say "most" or "least" the construction is article + noun + _____ / _____ + adjective.

3. The forms of **poder** are:

_____ _____

_____ _____

_____ _____

   The forms of **dormir** are:

_____ _____

_____ _____

_____ _____

Realidades Ⓑ

Capítulo 6B

Nombre _____

Fecha _____

Hora _____

Practice Workbook **6B–1**

Los cuartos

The Suárez family has just moved into a new house. Tell what rooms are on each floor of the house.

En la planta baja hay: _____

_____

_____

_____

En el primer piso hay: _____

_____

_____

_____

_____

Go Online WEB CODE jcd-0611
PHSchool.com

Los quehaceres

Each person below has been given a location from which to do his or her chores. In the spaces provided, list at least two chores each person could logically be doing. Follow the model.

| Modelo | Alberto y Antonio están en el garaje. |

lavan el coche

sacan la basura

limpian el garaje

1. Dolores está en el baño.

_____

_____

_____

2. Eugenio está en el dormitorio.

_____

_____

_____

3. Carolina y Catarina están en la sala.

_____

_____

_____

4. Vladimir está en el comedor.

_____

_____

_____

5. Ana Gracia está en la cocina.

_____

_____

_____

Realidades B

Capítulo 6B

Nombre _____

Hora _____

Fecha _____

Practice Workbook **6B–3**

La lista de quehaceres

Melisa's mom has left her a list of the things that she has to do before her relatives come over for a dinner party. Complete the list with the appropriate word or phrase. Follow the model.

Modelo _____*Arregla*_____ tu cuarto.

1. _____ la mesa del comedor.

2. Tienes que _____ porque no tienes ropa limpia.

3. _____ porque no tenemos platos limpios.

4. ¿Puedes _____? Hay demasiada basura.

5. _____ los platos en la cocina.

6. Necesitas _____ porque el coche está sucio.

7. Hay que _____ porque hay mucho polvo en el primer piso.

8. _____ las camas.

9. ¿Puedes _____ por las alfombras?

10. El baño no está limpio. Necesitas _____ .

11. _____ de comer al perro.

12. Si tienes tiempo, _____ todos los quehaceres.

Go Online WEB CODE jcd-0612
PHSchool.com

Realidades B

Capítulo 6B

Nombre _____

Hora _____

Fecha _____

Practice Workbook **6B–4**

No es correcto

The following statements do not make sense. Rewrite the sentences by replacing the underlined words or phrases with words or phrases that make sense. Follow the model.

Modelo	Nunca <u>haces</u> en casa cuando tienes quehaceres.

Nunca ayudas en casa cuando tienes quehaceres _____.

1. Tengo que <u>dar</u> la aspiradora por las alfombras.

   _____.

2. El cuarto está <u>limpio</u>. Voy a limpiarlo.

   _____.

3. Papá va a lavar platos en <u>el dormitorio</u>.

   _____.

4. No te <u>recibo</u> dinero porque no estás haciendo nada.

   _____.

5. <u>¡Haz la cama!</u> Vamos a comer.

   _____.

6. Mamá lava <u>el coche</u> en la cocina.

   _____.

7. ¿Cuáles son los <u>dinero</u> que tienes que hacer?

   _____.

8. Doy <u>dinero</u> al perro todos los días.

   _____.

9. Debes cortar <u>el polvo</u>, está bastante largo.

   _____.

10. Ernesto quita <u>el coche</u> de la sala.

    _____.

11. Las hermanas <u>cocinan</u> la basura por la noche.

    _____.

Realidades **B**

Capítulo 6B

Nombre _____

Fecha _____

Hora _____

Practice Workbook **6B–5**

Los mandatos

A. Write the affirmative **tú** command forms of the following verbs in the spaces provided.

1. correr _____

2. poner _____

3. hacer _____

4. comer _____

5. hablar _____

6. leer _____

7. limpiar _____

8. ver _____

9. cortar _____

10. abrir _____

11. escribir _____

B. Now, write the chore your parents might tell you to do in each of the following situations. Follow the model.

Modelo Tu dormitorio no está limpio.   _*Arregla tu dormitorio*_ .

1. El coche está sucio. _____ .

2. El perro tiene hambre. _____ .

3. No hay platos limpios. _____ .

4. Hay mucha basura en el garaje. _____ .

5. La camisa blanca ahora es gris. _____ .

6. Necesitamos cenar. _____ .

7. El baño no está limpio. _____ .

8. Hay mucho polvo en la sala. _____ .

Go Online WEB CODE jcd-0613
PHSchool.com

¿Qué están haciendo?

The Duarte family is getting ready for a barbecue. Look at the picture, then write what each of the family members is doing. Follow the model.

Modelo   La madre *está cocinando las hamburguesas* _____.

1. Manolo y José _____.

2. Ana María _____.

3. El padre _____.

4. Tito y Ramón _____.

5. Graciela _____.

6. Lola y Elia _____.

7. Todos _____.

Realidades B

Capítulo 6B

Nombre _____

Hora _____

Fecha _____

Practice Workbook **6B–7**

Macho trabajo

The Escobar family is getting ready to have guests over. Fill in the blanks in their conversation below with the appropriate form of the following verbs: **cortar, ayudar, hacer, lavar, pasar, sacar.**

PABLO: Mamá, ¿qué estás _____ tú?

MAMÁ: Estoy _____ los platos, hijo. ¿Y tú?

PABLO: Nada.

MAMÁ: Vale. ¿Qué están _____ tus hermanos?

PABLO: Juan está _____ el baño y Marta está arreglando

su dormitorio.

MAMÁ: Bien, hijo. Ahora, quita el polvo de la sala y luego _____

la aspiradora por las alfombras.

PABLO: Pero, mamá …

MAMÁ: ¡Ahora! Y después _____ la basura …

¡María! ¿Qué estás _____, hija?

MARÍA: Isabel y yo _____ el césped. ¿Por qué?

MAMÁ: Porque tus primos vienen a comer hoy y necesito ayuda para poner la mesa.

MARÍA: ¿Por qué no te está _____ papá?

MAMÁ: Papá, cariño, ¿dónde estás?

PAPÁ: Estoy en el garaje. Estoy _____ el coche.

MAMÁ: Ah, sí. Después, arregla nuestro cuarto y _____ tu ropa sucia.

PAPÁ: ¿Por qué?

MAMÁ: ¡Vienen tu hermano y su familia!

Go Online WEB CODE jcd-0615
PHSchool.com

Repaso

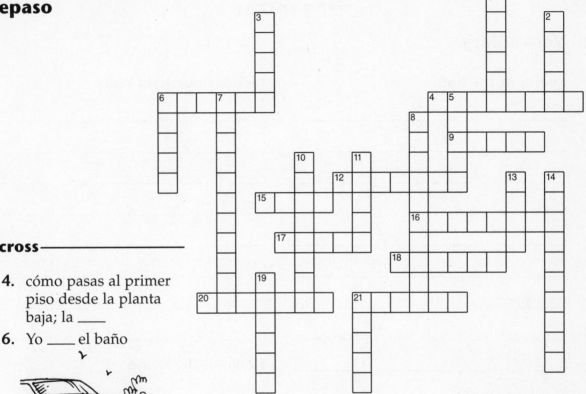

Across

4. cómo pasas al primer piso desde la planta baja; la ____

6. Yo ____ el baño

9.

12. *to cook*

15. El hijo ____ la aspiradora cada fin de semana.

16. ____ el cuarto

17. La hija debe ____ los platos ahora.

18. un cuarto donde puedes poner el coche

20. cuarto donde come la familia; el ____

21. el piso debajo de la planta baja

Down

1. el cuarto donde preparas la comida

2. Tengo que ____ la cama hoy.

3. quitar el ____

5. ____ la basura

6. no cerca

7. Después de subir la escalera, estás en el ____ .

8. Cuando entras en la casa, estás en la ____ ____ .

10. la oficina en la casa

11. ¿Quién va a ____ la mesa?

13. el cuarto donde ves la tele

14. el cuarto donde duermes

19. Mateo tiene que cortar el ____ .

21. no limpio

Realidades B

Capítulo 6B

Nombre _____

Hora _____

Fecha _____

Practice Workbook **6B–9**

Organizer

I. Vocabulary

Rooms of the house

_____
_____
_____
_____
_____
_____
_____
_____

Outdoor chores

_____
_____
_____
_____

Indoor household tasks

_____
_____
_____
_____
_____
_____

Floors of the house

_____
_____
_____
_____

II. Grammar

1. To talk about actions in progress, use the _____ tense. This is formed by adding -_____ to the roots of **-ar** verbs and -_____ to the roots of **-er** and **-ir** verbs.

2. **Tú** commands are the same as the _____ form of the _____ tense of verbs. But the **tú** command form of **poner** is _____ and of **hacer** is _____.

Go Online WEB CODE jcd-0616
PHSchool.com

Realidades **B**

Capítulo 7A

Nombre _____

Fecha _____

Hora _____

Practice Workbook **7A–1**

En el escaparate (*store window*)

You are window shopping at a large department store and you decide to make a list of what they have and what everything costs. Using the picture, list seven items and their prices below. Follow the model.

Modelo   *Los pantalones cuestan 35 dólares.*

1. _____

2. _____

3. _____

4. _____

5. _____

6. _____

7. _____

Realidades B

Capítulo 7A

Nombre _____

Hora _____

Fecha _____

Practice Workbook **7A–2**

Tienda de la Gracia

A. Write the numbers below in Spanish.

1. 100 _____

2. 500 _____

3. 909 _____

4. 222 _____

5. 767 _____

6. 676 _____

7. 110 _____

8. 881 _____

B. Read the following statistics about the chain of stores **Tienda de la Gracia**. Then answer the questions that follow.

TIENDA DE LA GRACIA	
Tiendas	100
Trabajadores	324
Promedio diario (*daily average*) de clientes	760
Camisas	612
Pantalones	404

1. ¿Cuántas Tiendas de la Gracia hay?

_____

2. ¿Cuál es el promedio diario de clientes en cada tienda?

_____

3. ¿Cuántos trabajadores hay en las Tiendas de la Gracia?

_____

4. ¿Cuántos pantalones hay en cada tienda?

_____

5. ¿Y camisas?

_____

Go Online WEB CODE jcd-0701
PHSchool.com

Realidades B

Capítulo 7A

Nombre _____

Hora _____

Fecha _____

Practice Workbook **7A–3**

En el centro comercial

Tatiana and Mariana are in the local mall. Write the words that most logically complete their conversation as they go from store to store.

TATIANA: Vamos a esta tienda de ropa. Aquí tienen _____ elegante.

MARIANA: Bien. ¿Qué _____ comprar?

TATIANA: Necesito un vestido para la fiesta de mi primo.

DEPENDIENTA: ¿En qué puedo _____, señorita?

TATIANA: _____ un vestido elegante.

DEPENDIENTA: ¿Va Ud. a _____ el vestido a una fiesta o un baile formal?

TATIANA: A una fiesta. Me gusta este vestido.

MARIANA: ¿Cómo te _____?

TATIANA: ¡Me queda fantástico! Quiero comprarlo.

MARIANA: Vamos a otra tienda. Necesito _____ unos zapatos

nuevos. Vamos a esa tienda, tienen buenos precios allí.

TATIANA: Mira estos zapatos aquí.

MARIANA: ¿Cuánto cuestan?

TATIANA: Trescientos dólares. ¿Es un buen _____?

MARIANA: Sí. Y me quedan _____. Voy a comprar estos zapatos.

TATIANA: Bien. Pasamos a otra tienda.

MARIANA: La tienda de música está a la derecha. ¿Entramos?

TATIANA: Sí, ¡_____!

Realidades B

Capítulo 7A

Nombre

Hora

Fecha

Practice Workbook **7A–4**

¿Qué llevan?

In complete sentences, describe two articles of clothing that each of the people below is wearing.

Pedro

A. _____

_____

B. _____

1. _____

Las hermanas Guzmán

A. _____

_____

B. _____

2. _____

La profesora Jones

A. _____

_____

B. _____

3. _____

El Dr. Cambambia

A. _____

_____

B. _____

4. _____

Anita

A. _____

_____

B. _____

5. _____

Go Online WEB CODE jcd-0702
PHSchool.com

Realidades B

Capítulo 7A

Nombre _____

Fecha _____

Hora _____

Practice Workbook **7A–5**

Algunos verbos nuevos

A. Fill in the chart below with the forms of the stem-changing verbs indicated.

	PENSAR	**QUERER**	**PREFERIR**
yo	*pienso*		
tú			*prefieres*
él, ella, Ud.		*quiere*	
nosotros			*preferimos*
vosotros	*pensáis*	*queréis*	*preferís*
ellos, ellas, Uds.		*quieren*	

B. Now, complete each sentence below by choosing the correct form of the verb **pensar**, **querer**, or **preferir**.

1. ¿ _____ (tú) la camisa roja o la camisa azul?

2. Nosotros _____ comprar un suéter nuevo.

3. Ellas _____ ir de compras hoy.

4. Vivian _____ llevar ropa elegante.

5. ¿Uds. _____ trabajar en la tienda de Mónica?

6. Yo _____ comprar los zapatos ahora.

7. Mis amigos y yo _____ jugar al fútbol cuando llueve.

8. Eduardo _____ ir a la fiesta con Brenda.

9. ¿Qué _____ (tú) hacer después de la escuela?

10. Marcelo y Claudio _____ ir al gimnasio después de la escuela.

11. Yo _____ buscar una bicicleta nueva.

12. ¿Tomás va a la tienda o _____ quedarse en casa?

WEB CODE jcd-0704
PHSchool.com

Realidades **B**

Capítulo 7A

Nombre _____

Hora _____

Fecha _____

Practice Workbook **7A–6**

¿Cuál prefieres?

A. Fill in the chart below with the singular and plural, masculine and feminine forms of the demonstrative adjectives.

este		estos	
	esa		esas

B. Complete the following questions about the clothing items pictured by writing in the appropriate demonstrative adjectives from the chart above. Then answer the questions by saying that you prefer the item indicated by the arrow.

1. —¿Prefieres _____ camisa o _____ suéter?

—_____

_____

2. —¿Prefieres _____ pantalones cortos o _____ jeans?

—_____

_____

3. —¿Te gustan más _____ sudaderas aquí o _____ suéteres?

—_____

_____

4. —¿Te gusta más _____ vestido o _____ falda?

—_____

_____

5. —¿Quieres _____ zapatos negros o _____ botas negras?

—_____

_____

6. —¿Prefieres _____ chaqueta o _____ abrigo?

—_____

_____

¿Quién?

Two sales associates are discussing some of the clients in their busy store. Fill in the blanks with the appropriate demonstrative adjectives based on the picture.

CELIA: ¿Qué hace _____ mujer allá?

YOLANDA: Pues, está mirando las botas, pero no quiere pagar mucho.

CELIA: ¿Qué quieren _____ mujeres aquí?

YOLANDA: Piensan comprar unos calcetines.

CELIA: ¿Y _____ hombre solo allí?

YOLANDA: ¿_____ hombre? Prefiere mirar los pantalones.

CELIA: A la derecha de él hay unos niños, ¿no? ¿Qué hacen _____ niños?

YOLANDA: Pues, _____ niños quieren unos suéteres nuevos.

CELIA: Oye, ¿ves a _____ hombres al lado de la puerta?

YOLANDA: Sí, piensan comprar _____ abrigos. ¿Por qué?

CELIA: Pues, son muy guapos, ¿no?

YOLANDA: Ah, sí. Creo que necesitan ayuda.

CELIA: ¡Hasta luego!

Realidades Ⓑ

Capítulo 7A

Nombre _____

Fecha _____

Hora _____

Practice Workbook **7A–8**

Repaso

Down ——————————

1.

2.

Across ——————————

2. Llevas ___ debajo de los zapatos.

3. ___ de baño

6. ¿Te ___ bien ese suéter?

7.

8. los ___ cortos

10. Yo llevo ___ en los pies.

12. No cuestan tanto. Es un buen ___.

14. En esta tienda, quiero ___ unas botas.

15. Jaime es informal. Siempre lleva camiseta y los ___.

17. Ella tiene que comprar un ___ para la fiesta.

18.

4. ¿Cuánto ___ las botas?

5. Mi padre es inteligente. Siempre tiene ___.

6. $5000 \div 10$

8. ___, señorita. Necesito ayuda.

9. Llevo una ___ en la cabeza.

11. Cuando hace frío, llevo un ___.

13. la ___ de ropa

16. 500×2

Realidades B

Capítulo 7A

Nombre _____

Hora _____

Fecha _____

Practice Workbook **7A–9**

Organizer

I. Vocabulary

Clothing for warm weather

_____

_____

_____

_____

_____

Clothing for cold weather

_____

_____

_____

_____

_____

_____

Other words to talk about clothing

_____

_____

_____

Numbers in the hundreds

_____

_____

_____

_____

_____

_____

II. Grammar

1. The forms of the verb **pensar** are: _____ _____

_____ _____

_____ _____

The forms of the verb **querer** are: _____ _____

_____ _____

_____ _____

The forms of the verb **preferir** are: _____ _____

_____ _____

_____ _____

2. To refer to something close, use _____ / _____, _____ / _____; to refer to something further away, use _____ / _____, _____ / _____

Go Online WEB CODE jcd-0706
PHSchool.com

Repaso del capítulo — *Vocabulario y gramática* **45**

Realidades Ⓑ

Capítulo 7B

Nombre _____

Fecha _____

Hora _____

Practice Workbook **7B–1**

Los regalos

Marcela is writing a list of gifts she wants to buy for her family. Help her by writing the names of the items suggested by the pictures in the blanks provided.

1. Para mi novio:

_____ _____ _____ _____

2. Para mi mejor amiga:

_____ _____

3. Para mi hermana:

_____ _____ _____ _____

4. Para mi padre:

_____ _____ _____

5. Para mi madre:

_____ _____ _____

Go Online WEB CODE jcd-0711
PHSchool.com

Realidades Ⓑ

Capítulo 7B

Nombre _____

Fecha _____

Hora _____

Practice Workbook **7B–2**

¡Tantas tiendas!

Write the names of the items pictured in the first blank, and where each person would find the items in the second blank.

1. Yo busco _____

   en una _____.

2. Germán busca _____

   en una _____.

3. Tú buscas _____

   en la _____.

4. Mi hermano busca _____

   en la _____.

5. Bárbara busca _____

   en un _____.

6. Buscamos _____

   en la _____.

7. Esteban y Luis buscan un _____

   en la _____.

8. Susana y Paulina buscan _____

   en una _____.

9. —¿En dónde puedo comprar _____?

   —En un _____

Realidades **B**

Capítulo 7B

Nombre _____

Hora _____

Fecha _____

Practice Workbook **7B–3**

¿El regalo perfecto?

Valentine's Day is coming and Pepe and Laura are deciding what gifts to give each other.

A. Read the conversations below.

(*En una tienda de descuentos*)

PEPE: Necesito comprar un regalo para mi novia.
DEPENDIENTE: ¿Qué piensa comprar?
PEPE: No sé. Tiene que ser algo barato porque no tengo mucho dinero.
DEPENDIENTE: Pero, ¿no quiere un anillo bonito o un collar elegante para su novia?
PEPE: No. Es demasiado.
DEPENDIENTE: Puede comprar un reloj pulsera que no cuesta tanto.
PEPE: Oiga, el mes pasado compré software nuevo para mi computadora, para poder jugar videojuegos en la Red. ¡Pagué unos 90 dólares!
DEPENDIENTE: Entonces quiere este llavero de veinte dólares.
PEPE: ¡Genial!

(*En un almacén*)

LAURA: Quiero el regalo perfecto para mi novio.
DEPENDIENTA: ¿Él trabaja? ¿Quizás una corbata bonita?
LAURA: Estoy pensando en un regalo más romántico . . .
DEPENDIENTA: ¿Unos guantes para las noches de frío?
LAURA: No creo. Él nunca tiene frío. ¿Ud. tiene algo romántico?
DEPENDIENTA: ¡Mire! ¿Qué piensa de este anillo de cincuenta dólares?
LAURA: ¡Perfecto! Quiero uno, por favor.

B. Answer the questions about the dialogues in complete sentences.

1. ¿A qué tienda va Pepe? _____

   ¿Qué busca allí? ¿Por qué? _____

2. ¿Qué quiere venderle el dependiente? ¿Por qué Pepe no quiere comprarlos?

   _____

   _____

3. ¿Qué compra por fin Pepe? _____

4. ¿Qué quiere comprar Laura? _____

5. ¿Por qué Laura no quiere ni una corbata ni unos guantes? _____

   _____

6. ¿Qué va a comprar Laura? _____ ¿Es más

   caro o más barato que el regalo de Pepe? _____

Realidades (B)

Capítulo 7B

Nombre _____

Hora _____

Fecha _____

Practice Workbook **7B–4**

Oraciones desordenadas

Put the scrambled sentences below into logical order.

1. compré / hace / lo / semana / una

   _____

2. yo / por / ayer / unos / pagué / un / guantes / dólar

   _____

3. lector / caro / DVD / un / es / muy / no

   _____

4. joyas / en / venden / almacén / el

   _____

5. pasada / la / compré / yo / semana / suéter / nuevo / un

   _____

6. anoche / una / compré / computadora / yo / nueva

   _____

7. pagaste / el / collar / cuánto / por

   ¿_____?

8. lo / año / el / tú / compraste / pasado

   _____

9. joyas / por / venden / tienda / esta / veinte / en / dólares

   _____

10. cuánto / por / el / pagaste / reloj

    ¿_____?

Realidades B

Capítulo 7B

Nombre _____

Hora _____

Fecha _____

Practice Workbook **7B–5**

Hablamos del pasado

A. Fill in the chart below with the preterite forms of the verbs indicated.

	COMPRAR	HABLAR	PREPARAR	USAR	MIRAR
yo	compré				
tú					miraste
él, ella, Ud.		habló			
nosotros				usamos	
vosotros	comprasteis	hablasteis	preparasteis	usasteis	mirasteis
ellos, ellas, Uds.			prepararon		

B. Fill in the blanks in the following postcard with the correct preterite forms of the verbs given.

¡Hola, mamá!

    ¿Cómo estás? Estoy muy bien aquí en Quito.
Primero, José y yo _____ (preparar) unos
sándwiches ricos y _____ (hablar) con su
mamá un poco. Después, decidimos ir al centro
comercial. José y su mamá _____ (mirar)
unas chaquetas en la tienda de Smith y yo
_____ (comprar) algunas cosas para la
semana.

    A las cinco, la mamá de José _____
(llamar) por teléfono al padre, y él _____
(regresar) del trabajo un poco después. Nosotros
_____ (cenar) y _____ (usar) la
computadora antes de dormir.

    ¿Y tú? ¿ _____ (caminar) esta semana?
¿ _____ (comprar) el regalo para el
cumpleaños de papi? Pues, nos vemos en una semana.
¡Mañana me voy a Lima!

        Un abrazo,
        Víctor

La Sra. Guiraldo
Vía Águila 1305
Col. Cuauhtémoc
06500 México, D.F.

Go Online WEB CODE jcd-0713
PHSchool.com

Realidades **B**

Capítulo 7B

Nombre

Fecha

Hora

Practice Workbook **7B–6**

Mini-conversaciones

A. Fill in the following charts with the preterite forms of the verbs given.

	PAGAR	BUSCAR	JUGAR	PRACTICAR	TOCAR
yo	pagué			practiqué	
tú			jugaste		
él, ella, Ud.		buscó			
nosotros					tocamos
vosotros	pagasteis	buscasteis	jugasteis	practicasteis	tocasteis
ellos, ellas, Uds.				practicaron	

B. Now, complete the mini-conversations below with preterite verb forms from the chart above.

1. —Juan, ¿cuánto _____ por tu suéter?

   —Yo _____ 25 dólares.

2. —¿Qué hizo Marta anoche?

   —Ella _____ al fútbol con sus hermanos.

3. —Hija, ¿_____ el piano?

   —Sí, mamá. _____ por una hora.

4. —Busco un apartamento nuevo.

   —Yo _____ por un año antes de encontrar el apartamento perfecto.

5. —¿Uds. _____ un instrumento en el pasado?

   —Sí, nosotros _____ el violín.

6. —¿Marcos va a practicar el básquetbol hoy?

   —No, él _____ toda la semana pasada.

7. —¿Con quién _____ (tú) al golf?

   —_____ con mis dos hermanos y con mi padre.

Realidades Ⓑ

Capítulo 7B

Nombre _____

Fecha _____

Hora _____

Practice Workbook **7B–7**

Objeto directo

A. Rewrite the following sentences about shopping using direct object pronouns in place of the appropriate nouns.

1. Compré los zapatos. _____

2. ¿Tienes el vestido verde? _____

3. Escribo el cuento. _____

4. Mi mamá recibe el dinero. _____

5. Las mujeres llevan las faldas nuevas. _____

6. ¿Rosario va a comprar el regalo? _____

7. Las amigas compraron aretes nuevos. _____

8. Llevo los dos abrigos. _____

B. Ramona's mother is talking to her about their trip to the mall. Answer her questions using direct object pronouns. Follow the model.

Modelo   ¿Llevas tu vestido nuevo a la escuela?

Sí, lo llevo mucho.

1. ¿Dónde vas a poner tu camisa nueva?

_____

2. ¿Compraste los zapatos azules?

_____

3. ¿Usas el reloj pulsera negro?

_____

4. ¿Cuándo vas a llevar tus guantes nuevos?

_____

5. ¿Tienes las camisetas nuevas?

_____

Realidades **B**

Capítulo 7B

Nombre _____

Fecha _____

Hora _____

Practice Workbook **7B–8**

Repaso

Across

5. donde las mujeres ponen las llaves, bolígrafos, etc.

7. la ____ de electrodomésticos

8. tienda donde venden zapatos

13.

14. los ____ de sol

17. Una tienda de ropa es donde ____ ropa.

18. no caro

20. tienda donde venden joyas

Down

1. Llevo los ____ durante el invierno porque tengo las manos frías.

2. Sancho quiere ____ las fotos de tu viaje.

3.

4. donde pones el dinero y a veces unas fotos; la ____

6. tienda donde venden libros

9. joya que llevas en las orejas

10. tienda donde venden todo

11. tipo de reloj que llevas en el cuerpo; reloj ____

12. donde pones las llaves

15. joya que llevas en el dedo

16. Los hombres llevan una camisa con ____ al trabajo.

19. *last night*

Realidades **B**

Capítulo 7B

Nombre _____

Hora _____

Fecha _____

Practice Workbook **7B–9**

Organizer

I. Vocabulary

Types of stores

_____

_____

_____

_____

_____

Words to talk about jewelry

_____

_____

_____

_____

_____

Other gifts

_____

_____

_____

_____

Words to talk about the past

_____

_____

_____

_____

_____

II. Grammar

1. The preterite endings of **-ar** verbs are: -_____   -_____

    -_____   -_____

    -_____   -_____

    Now conjugate the verb **pasar** in the preterite: _____   _____

    _____   _____

    _____   _____

2. The preterite ending of the **yo** form of verbs ending with **-car** is -_____ . For **-gar** verbs it is -_____ .

3. The direct object pronouns are _____ , _____ , _____ , and _____ .

Go Online WEB CODE jcd-0717
PHSchool.com

Realidades B

Capítulo 8A

Nombre _____

Hora _____

Fecha _____

Practice Workbook **8A–1**

¿Adónde van?

Complete the mini-conversations. Use the drawing to fill in the first blank and to give you a clue for the second blank. Follow the model.

Modelo

—¿Viste el _____*monumento*_____ nuevo de Cristóbal Colón?

—Sí, ¡es fantástico! Está enfrente del _____*museo*_____.

1. —Mamá, quiero ver _____.

—Sí, Marisol. Vamos al _____.

2. —¿Uds. van de vacaciones en _____ este verano?

—No, vamos a la _____.

3. —¿Vas a ver _____ hoy?

—Sí, mis padres y yo vamos al _____.

4. —¿Quieres _____ hoy?

—Sí, pero ¿en dónde? ¿En el _____?

5. —¿Dónde es el _____?

—Pues, en el _____, por supuesto.

6. —¿Cómo te gusta ir de _____?

—Siempre viajamos en _____.

Asociaciones

A. Write the names of the places from your vocabulary that you associate with the following things or actions.

1. la historia, el arte __ __ __ Ⓞ __ __ __ __ Ⓞ

2. las atracciones, los monos __ __ __ Ⓞ __ __ __ __

3. pintar, dibujar, el arte __ __ Ⓞ __ __

4. divertido, personas atrevidas, jugar __ __ Ⓞ __ __ __ __ __

   __ __ __ Ⓞ __ __ __ Ⓞ __

5. los deportes, un partido, ver Ⓞ __ __ __ Ⓞ __ __

6. la obra, el actor __ Ⓞ __ __ __ __

7. el hotel, muchas personas Ⓞ __ __ __ __ __

8. pasear en bote, mucha agua __ __ __ Ⓞ

B. Now, unscramble the circled letters to find a related word.

__ __ __ __ __ __ __ __ __ __

Go Online WEB CODE jcd-0801
PHSchool.com

¡Vamos al parque nacional!

The Carreras family went on vacation to Rocky Mountain National Park in Colorado. Read the postcard they sent to their friends back home and fill in the blanks with the words suggested by the pictures.

¡Saludos desde Colorado!

Llegamos al _____ el lunes pasado. Yo fui directamente

a la playa para _____ . El _____

es precioso y ¡los _____ son enormes! El martes paseamos

en _____ por el lago y miramos los _____

. ¡Yo vi un oso en el bosque!

Para mañana tenemos muchos planes. Vamos a _____

por las montañas y por la noche vamos al _____ para ver

una obra musical.

Regresamos a la _____ el viernes. ¡Nos vemos

este fin de semana!

Abrazos,

Familia Carreras

Realidades B

Capítulo 8A

Nombre _____

Hora _____

Fecha _____

Practice Workbook **8A–4**

¿Qué te pasó?

A. Read the dialogue between Aníbal and Carmen about Aníbal's trip to the beach.

CARMEN: Dime, ¿fuiste a la playa con tus primos?

ANÍBAL: ¡Ay, amiga; fue un desastre! Salí muy temprano para pasar todo el día allí.

Durante el día tomamos el sol y buceamos en el mar.

CARMEN: ¿No fue un día tremendo para descansar y pasarlo bien con tus amigos?

ANÍBAL: Por dos horas, sí. Pero después de mucha lluvia, todo salió mal.

CARMEN: Lo siento. Va a hacer buen tiempo este sábado. . .

ANÍBAL: Bueno, tú y yo podemos salir de la ciudad.

CARMEN: ¡Genial!

B. Now, answer the questions in complete sentences.

1. ¿Adónde fue Aníbal? _____

_____

2. ¿Qué hizo allí? _____

_____

3. ¿Con quién fue Aníbal? _____

_____

4. ¿Qué tiempo va a hacer el sábado? _____

_____

5. ¿Qué van a hacer Aníbal y Carmen? _____

_____

Go Online WEB CODE jcd-0802
PHSchool.com

¿Qué hicieron?

A. Fill in the chart with the preterite forms of the verbs given.

	COMER	ESCRIBIR	CORRER	SALIR	VER	BEBER
yo	comí				vi	
tú			corriste			
él, ella, Ud.				salió		bebió
nosotros		escribimos				
vosotros	comisteis	escribisteis	corristeis	salisteis	visteis	bebisteis
ellos/as, Uds.						

B. Now, complete the mini-conversations below by filling in the appropriate forms of one of the verbs from Part A.

1. —Pablo, ¿vas a correr hoy?

   —No, _____ ayer.

2. —¿Elena _____ toda la leche?

   —Sí, toda.

3. —¿Uds. salieron anoche?

   —Sí, _____ a las once.

4. —¿_____ la nueva película de Almodóvar?

   —Sí, la vi anoche.

5. —¡Qué buenos niños!

   —Sí, _____ todas las zanahorias.

6. —Juan, escribe la tarea.

   —Ya la _____ , mamá.

7. —¿Uds. comieron en el hotel anoche?

   —No, _____ en el restaurante.

8. —¿Quién va a correr en el maratón este año?

   —Todos, porque sólo dos personas _____ el año pasado.

9. —¿Con quién saliste, Marta?

   —_____ con Toño.

10. —¿El autor va a escribir un cuento nuevo?

    —No, él _____ uno el mes pasado.

Realidades Ⓑ

Capítulo 8A

Nombre _____

Hora _____

Fecha _____

Practice Workbook **8A–6**

¿Adónde fueron?

Some friends are talking about where they went on vacation. Write where they went, using the pictures below to help you. Follow the model.

Modelo La familia Madrigal _fue al zoológico_____.

1. Carlos _____.

2. Yo _____.

3. Lola y Tina _____.

4. Nosotros _____.

5. Elisa _____.

6. Tú _____.

7. Uds. _____.

Go Online WEB CODE jcd-0804
PHSchool.com

Realidades ⓑ

Capítulo 8A

Nombre _____

Fecha _____

Hora _____

Practice Workbook **8A–7**

¿Qué viste?

Alicia saw many things at the park yesterday. Use the drawing and the location clues to say whom or what she saw. Pay attention to the use of the personal **a** in your statements. Follow the model.

Modelo En el parque ayer, yo vi ___*a unos amigos*___ corriendo.

1. Yo vi _____ dándoles de comer a unos pájaros.

2. Yo vi _____ jugando al fútbol.

3. Yo vi _____ en la mesa.

4. En el lago, yo vi _____ paseando.

5. En el bote, yo vi _____ con una señorita.

6. En un árbol yo vi _____.

7. Al lado del árbol vi _____.

8. Debajo del árbol vi _____ con pelo largo.

9. En la playa vi _____.

Realidades

Capítulo 8A

Nombre _____

Hora _____

Fecha _____

Practice Workbook **8A–8**

Repaso

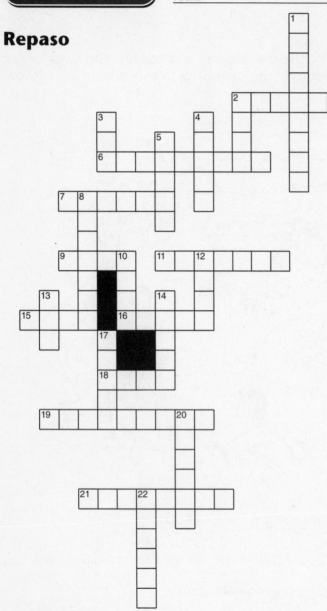

Down ——————————————

1. Me gusta ___ en el sofá.
2. donde puedes pasear en bote; el ___
3. Yo quiero ___ la tele.
4. medio de transporte que va por el agua; el ___
5. un edificio con muchos cuadros; el ___
8. medio de transporte que usan los estudiantes para ir a la escuela; el ___
10. la ___ de teatro
12. *the train*; el ___
13. *the sea*; el ___
14. sinónimo de **vacaciones**; un ___

17.

20. Chicago es una ___ donde hace mucho viento.

22.

Across ——————————————

2. *place*; un ___
6. En el monumento, compramos ___.
7. el ___ de diversiones

9.

11. donde se juegan los partidos de fútbol; el ___
15. España es un ___ donde hablan español.
16. medio de transporte que va por el aire; el ___
18. pasear en ___
19. donde hay atracciones de animales; el ___
21. no tarde

Realidades **B**

Capítulo 8A

Nombre _____

Hora _____

Fecha _____

Practice Workbook **8A–9**

Organizer

I. Vocabulary

Places to visit

_____

_____

_____

_____

Modes of transportation

_____

_____

_____

_____

Leisure activities

_____

_____

_____

_____

Phrases to discuss experiences

_____

_____

_____

_____

II. Grammar

1. The preterite endings of **-er** and **-ir** verbs are:

   yo -_____   nosotros -_____

   tú -_____   vosotros -_isteis_

   Ud. -_____   Uds. -_____

2. The preterite forms of **ir** (and **ser**) are: _____ _____

   _____ _____

   _____ _____

3. _____ is inserted before the direct object of a sentence if the direct object is

   a person. This is called the _____.

La comunidad

Your new friend in Costa Rica is showing you around her community. Label each place or point of interest in the picture with the appropriate word.

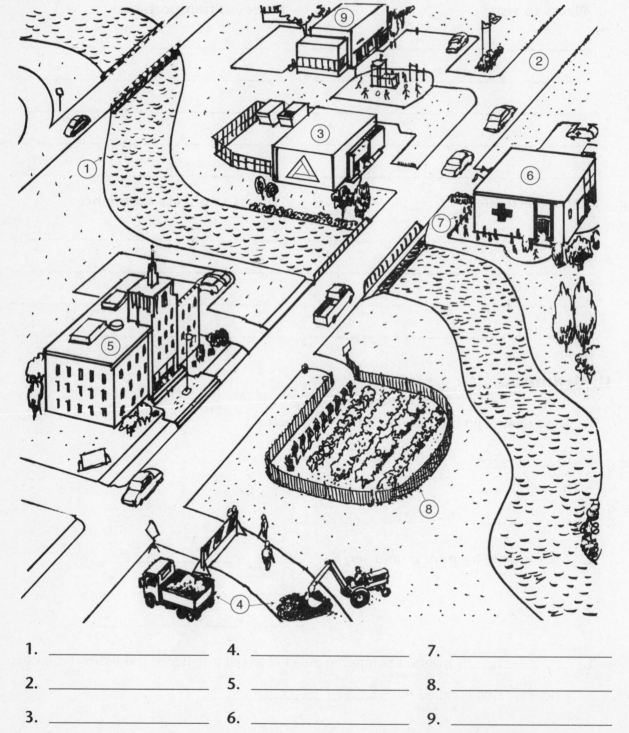

1. _____   4. _____   7. _____

2. _____   5. _____   8. _____

3. _____   6. _____   9. _____

Go Online WEB CODE jcd-0811
PHSchool.com

Realidades B

Capítulo 8B

Nombre _____

Fecha _____

Hora _____

Practice Workbook **8B-2**

El reciclaje

A. Your community is starting a recycling program. Label each item below with words from your vocabulary.

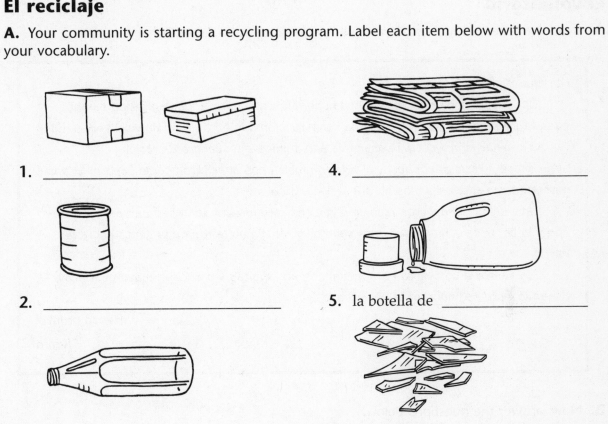

1. _____

2. _____

3. _____

4. _____

5. la botella de _____

6. la botella de _____

B. Now, write sentences to say whether or not it is necessary to recycle the items below. Follow the model.

Modelo   Los tomates *No es necesario reciclar los tomates.* _____

1. El helado _____

2. El plástico _____

3. El vidrio _____

4. La sala _____

5. Las latas _____

Realidades B

Capítulo 8B

Nombre _____

Hora _____

Fecha _____

Practice Workbook **8B-3**

El voluntario

A. Read the letter below from Álvaro, who is working as an AmeriCorps volunteer.

Querida familia:

¡Qué experiencia! Hacemos tantas cosas para ayudar a los demás. La semana pasada ayudamos en un proyecto de construcción con otro grupo de voluntarios. Ellos van a terminar el proyecto. Después de eso, fuimos a un centro de reciclaje. Allí aprendimos a reciclar el papel y el vidrio. También nos enseñaron cómo separar el papel normal (como el papel de los libros) de los periódicos.

Esta semana nosotros recogimos mucha ropa usada de varias partes de la ciudad y la llevamos a un centro para pobres. Allí le dimos la ropa a la gente pobre del barrio.

Hoy vamos a un centro para ancianos para ayudar a personas mayores. Estoy cansado, pero es importante hacer esto.

¡Hasta pronto!

~Ívaro

B. Now, answer the questions below.

1. ¿Cuántas cosas hace Álvaro para ayudar a los demás? ¿Cuáles son? _____

    _____

    _____

2. ¿Qué aprendió Álvaro en el centro de reciclaje? _____

    _____

3. ¿Adónde llevaron Álvaro y los voluntarios la ropa usada? _____

    _____

4. ¿A quiénes le dieron la ropa? _____

    _____

5. ¿Qué hace Álvaro hoy? _____

    _____

Go Online WEB CODE jcd-0812
PHSchool.com

Realidades B

Capítulo 8B

Nombre _____

Hora _____

Fecha _____

Practice Workbook **8B–4**

¿Qué haces en la comunidad?

You overhear two friends telling their teacher about what they do to help out in their communities. You can't hear what the teacher is asking. Fill in the teacher's questions. Follow the model.

Modelo — *¿Uds. ayudan en la comunidad?*

      —Sí, trabajamos como voluntarios en la comunidad.

—¿_____?

—Trabajamos en una escuela primaria. Les enseñamos a los niños a leer.

—¿_____?

—También recogemos ropa usada.

—¿_____?

—Recogemos la ropa usada del barrio.

—¿_____?

—Hay que separar la ropa y después lavarla.

—¿_____?

—Le damos la ropa usada a la gente pobre del barrio.

—¿_____?

—Sí, ayudamos en el hospital.

—¿_____?

—Trabajamos como voluntarios en un hospital para niños. Nos encanta el trabajo voluntario.

Realidades (B)

Capítulo 8B

Nombre _____

Hora _____

Fecha _____

Practice Workbook **8B–5**

¿Quién dice qué?

The people in the chart below are concerned citizens. Tell what each says by combining the subject on the left with the phrase on the right using **decir + que**. Follow the model.

Subjects	Phrases
Smokey the Bear	Hay que tener cuidado en el campamento.
Los directores del centro de reciclaje	Es necesario separar el plástico y el vidrio.
Gloria	La gente tiene que limpiar el barrio.
Yo	Todos deben participar en las actividades de la comunidad.
La profesora	Es esencial hacer trabajo voluntario.
La Cruz Roja	Es importante ayudar a los enfermos.
Tú	Es importante llevar la ropa usada a centros para los pobres.
Mi familia y yo	Es importante reciclar las botellas y latas.

Modelo   *Smokey the Bear dice que hay que tener cuidado en el campamento.*

1. _____

2. _____

3. _____

4. _____

5. _____

6. _____

7. _____

Go Online WEB CODE jcd-0813
PHSchool.com

Realidades Ⓑ

Capítulo 8B

Nombre _____

Hora _____

Fecha _____

Practice Workbook **8B–6**

Más trabajo voluntario

A. Write the indirect object pronouns that correspond to the following phrases.

1. A Javier y a Sara _____

2. A Diego y a mí _____

3. A la Dra. Estes _____

4. A Uds. _____

5. A Tito _____

6. A Luz y a ti _____

7. A ti _____

8. A nosotros _____

9. Al Sr. Pérez _____

10. A mí _____

B. Now, fill in the blanks in the following sentences with the correct indirect object pronouns.

1. La Cruz Roja _____ ayuda a las personas de la comunidad.

2. Nuestros padres _____ hablaron a mi hermano y a mí del reciclaje.

3. Mi profesora _____ ayudó a decidir qué trabajo voluntario me gustaría

   hacer.

4. _____ dice el profesor al estudiante que es importante separar las latas

   y el plástico.

5. Las personas _____ escriben al director del centro de reciclaje para

   recibir información sobre el reciclaje.

6. ¿Tus padres _____ dicen que debes ayudar a los demás?

7. _____ traigo unos juguetes a los niños en el hospital.

8. Los ancianos están muy contentos cuando _____ decimos que

   volvemos mañana.

Realidades **B**

Capítulo 8B

Nombre _____

Hora _____

Fecha _____

Practice Workbook **8B–7**

¿Hacer o dar?

A. Fill in the chart below with the correct forms of **hacer** and **dar** in the preterite.

	HACER	DAR
yo	hice	di
tú		
él, ella, Ud.		
nosotros		
vosotros	hicisteis	disteis
ellos, ellas, Uds.		

B. Now, fill in the blanks in the telephone conversation below with the appropriate forms from the chart above.

LEYDIN: ¡Mamá, estoy aquí en los Estados Unidos!

MADRE: Hola, hija. ¿Cómo estás?

LEYDIN: Bien, mamá. Yo _____ muchas cosas ayer después de llegar.

MADRE: ¿Qué _____?

LEYDIN: Pues, primero les _____ los regalos a toda la familia.

MADRE: ¿Y la abuelita te _____ un regalo a ti, también?

LEYDIN: Sí, ¡una bicicleta nueva! Estoy muy contenta.

MADRE: Y, ¿qué _____ Uds. después?

LEYDIN: Los primos _____ la tarea y la abuelita y yo le _____ la lista de cosas que comprar para la cena. Después le _____ la lista al abuelo, quien _____ las compras en el supermercado.

MADRE: ¿_____ Uds. algo más?

LEYDIN: Sí. Después de comer, yo _____ un postre especial para todos: ¡tu famoso pastel de tres leches!

MADRE: ¡Qué coincidencia! Yo _____ uno también y les _____ un poco a nuestros amigos, los Sánchez. ¿Qué más . . .?

Go Online WEB CODE jcd-0814
PHSchool.com

Realidades (B)

Capítulo 8B

Nombre _____

Fecha _____

Hora _____

Practice Workbook **8B-8**

Repaso

Across

2. Es importante ____ las botellas usadas de las calles.

4. Es necesario ayudar a los ____.

6. otra ____

10. *unforgettable*

13. el ____ de construcción

15.

16. lugar donde recogen las verduras y las plantas; el ____

20. AmeriCorps hace el trabajo ____.

22. Esa ____ es de cartón.

24. *problem*

Down

1. *poor*

3. Puedes reciclar una ____ de vidrio o de plástico.

5. *often*; ____ ____

7. Puedes reciclar las botellas de ____ y de plástico.

8. Es importante reciclar las cajas de ____.

9. sinónimo de **las personas**; la ____

11. Los ____ son nuestro futuro.

12. el ____ de reciclaje

13.

14. El profesor ____ las botellas al centro de reciclaje.

17. el ____ Grande

18. *toy*; un ____

19. Mis padres me ____ la verdad.

21. sinónimo de **la comunidad**; el ____

23.

Realidades **B**

Capítulo 8B

Nombre _____

Hora _____

Fecha _____

Practice Workbook **8B–9**

Organizer

I. Vocabulary

Places to do volunteer work

_____

_____

_____

_____

_____

Things that are recyclable

_____

_____

_____

_____

_____

Verbs to talk about recycling

_____

_____

_____

Words to describe experiences

_____

_____

_____

II. Grammar

1. The forms of **decir** in the present are: _____ _____

   _____ _____

   _____ _____

2. The indirect object pronouns are: _____ _____

   _____ _____

   _____ _____

3. The preterite forms of **dar** are: _____ _____

   _____ _____

   _____ _____

   The preterite forms of **hacer** are: _____ _____

   _____ _____

   _____ _____

Go Online WEB CODE jcd-0817
PHSchool.com

Nombre _____

Hora _____

Fecha _____

Las películas

A. You love movies, but always forget to check the newspaper for the showings. You constantly have to ask your friends what movies are showing and at what time. Complete each dialogue by filling in the words that best identify the picture.

1. —¿Cuándo empieza la _____?

   —Empieza a las nueve y media. Son casi las nueve. ¡Vamos ahora!

2. —¿Va a ser larga la _____?

   —Sí. Empieza a las dos y media y termina a las cinco menos cuarto.

3. —¿A qué hora dan la _____?

   —A las seis.

4. —¿Cuánto dura el _____?

   —Dura menos de tres horas.

5. —¿Cuándo va a empezar la _____?

   —Empieza a las cuatro y media.

6. —Ya es la una y veinte. ¿Qué podemos hacer?

   —Podemos ir al cine a ver una _____.

B. Now, say the following time expressions another way using new vocabulary phrases.

1. Son las cinco menos diez. _____.

2. Son las dos y treinta. _____.

3. Dura una hora y cincuenta minutos. Dura _____.

4. Termina a las once y cuarenta. Termina _____.

Realidades **B**

Capítulo 9A

Nombre _____

Fecha _____

Hora _____

Practice Workbook **9A–2**

¿Qué programas les gustan?

Read the information about each person below. Then decide which TV program would be best for him or her and write it in the blank.

1. Pedro es gracioso. Siempre cuenta chistes y hace cosas cómicas. A él le gustan

   los programas _____.

2. Mi padre lee el periódico todos los días. Le interesa la política. A él le gustan

   los programas _____.

3. La profesora tiene dos hijos y quiere enseñarles mucho. También busca información

   para usar en la clase. Ella prefiere los programas _____.

4. Abuela no trabaja y tiene que estar en casa. Le interesan mucho los

   juegos, especialmente cuando la gente gana dinero. A ella le gustan los programas

   _____.

5. Javi toca la guitarra y Juanita canta. Pasan casi todo el tiempo practicando la

   música. A ellos les gustan los programas _____.

6. Rosa estudia inglés. Un día quiere trabajar para un periódico. Para aprender más

   de la gente, ella ve los programas _____.

7. Ronaldo es deportista. Juega al fútbol, al béisbol y al básquetbol. Cuando no está

   practicando un deporte está viendo programas _____.

8. A Cristina le gustan las historias. Lee novelas románticas y a veces escribe cuentos

   de amor. A ella le gustan las _____.

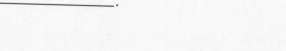 Go Online WEB CODE jcd-0901 PHSchool.com

Realidades Ⓑ

Capítulo 9A

Nombre _____

Fecha _____

Hora _____

Practice Workbook **9A–3**

¿Cómo son las cosas allí?

Luzma is writing a letter to her pen pal in the U.S. She is telling her pen pal about TV and movies in her country. Fill in the blanks with the words that best complete her thoughts.

Querida Valerie,

     ¿Qué tal? ¿Cómo fue la _____ que viste la semana pasada? En

mi país me encanta ir al cine. Me gustan más las películas _____.

Mi hermano es policía y _____ yo sé mucho _____

los policías. También me interesa esta clase de películas porque son más

_____ que una comedia o la ciencia ficción. Las comedias

_____ aburren y a veces son infantiles. No me gustan las películas

de _____ porque son demasiado violentas. ¿Qué _____

película te gusta más a ti?

     Ahora te hablo de los _____ de televisión aquí. Bueno, no son

muy diferentes de los programas de allí. Tenemos programas de dibujos

animados como Rin, ran, run, programas de _____ como ¡Una

fortuna para ti! y tenemos las noticias. Yo veo las noticias pero sólo me

interesan los programas que dan sobre la policía en el _____ 56.

     Eso es todo. Adiós, amiga.

                                Luzma

Realidades **B**

Capítulo 9A

Nombre _____

Hora _____

Fecha _____

Practice Workbook **9A–4**

Tus programas favoritos

Read the TV listings below, then answer the questions that follow in complete sentences.

EVENING — NOCHE		
6PM		
2 Noticias	**8PM**	**2** ¡Niágara!
18 Amigos		**18** Amigos
26 Noticias		**26** Película: El monstruo verde
30 Pepito y Paquito		**30** El mundo real
33 Mi casa		**33** Hoy día
42 Deportivas		**42** Fútbol . . . .
60 Música cubana		**60** ¿Puedes cantar?
7pm **2** Los monos	**9PM**	**2** El zoológico
18 Noticias		**18** Mi Amiga Sara
26 Entre tú y yo		**26** . . . .
30 Noticias		**30** El día en Alaska
33 Noticias		**33** ¡Ganar un coche!
42 Deportes		**42** . . . .
60 La salsa y la samba		**60** Baile en vivo

1. ¿Cuántos programas de noticias empiezan a las seis? _____

2. ¿Qué clase de programas tiene el canal 42? _____

   ¿Y el canal 60? _____

   ¿Y el canal 2? _____

3. ¿Qué programa deportivo puedes ver a las ocho? _____

   _____

4. Para ver un programa educativo, ¿vas a ver el canal 2 o el 18 a las ocho? _____

   _____

5. ¿Qué clase de programa empieza a las nueve en el canal 33? _____

   ¿Y a las nueve en el canal 30? _____

6. ¿Qué clase de programa dan a las siete en el canal 26? _____

7. ¿Dan una película de horror a las ocho en el canal 26?

   _____

Go Online WEB CODE jcd-0902
PHSchool.com

Realidades B

Capítulo 9A

Nombre _____

Hora _____

Fecha _____

Practice Workbook **9A–5**

Acabo de . . .

Write what the following people just finished doing and are now going to do, based on the pictures. Follow the model.

Modelo Marta _acaba de estudiar. Ahora va a dormir._

1. Anabel _____
_____

2. Nosotros _____
_____

3. Ellas _____
_____

4. Yo _____
_____

5. Tú _____
_____

6. Juan y el Sr. Lebredo _____
_____

7. Roberto _____
_____

8. Ana María _____
_____

Más gustos

A. Complete the sentences below with the correct forms of the verbs given.

1. Al Presidente le _____ (interesar) la política.

2. ¡Qué terrible! Me _____ (doler) el pie izquierdo.

3. A los estudiantes les _____ (aburrir) las presentaciones largas.

4. A nosotros nos _____ (encantar) ver comedias.

5. A tus hermanos les _____ (gustar) las películas de horror.

6. A ti te _____ (interesar) el teatro.

7. Me _____ (quedar) bien los pantalones pero me

_____ (faltar) el dinero para comprarlos.

B. Now, complete each sentence below with the correct form of the verb given and the appropriate indirect object pronoun. Follow the model.

Modelo A Carlos _____*le aburre*_____ (aburrir) la política.

1. A mí _____ (faltar) un lápiz.

2. A ellas _____ (aburrir) las clases de arte.

3. A Carmen _____ (quedar) bien la falda, ¿no?

4. A ti _____ (encantar) los programas deportivos.

5. ¿A ti y a Pedro _____ (gustar) leer revistas?

6. A mi papá _____ (doler) los pies.

7. ¿A Ud. _____ (faltar) los cuadernos?

8. A nosotros _____ (interesar) las obras de teatro.

9. A Lola y a Roberto _____ (interesar) el programa musical y el programa educativo.

Go **Online** WEB CODE jcd-0904
PHSchool.com

Realidades **B**

Capítulo 9A

Nombre _____

Fecha _____

Hora _____

Practice Workbook **9A–7**

Frases revueltas

The following sentences are mixed up. Rearrange them so that they are grammatically correct and make sense. Don't forget to conjugate verbs where appropriate. Follow the model.

Modelo   ir al cine / me / a mí / y al centro comercial / gustar

A mí me gusta ir al cine y al centro comercial.

1. le / leer / a Elena / poemas / encantar / y escribir

_____

2. negros / unos zapatos / te / para / faltar / a ti / ir a la fiesta

_____

3. diez kilómetros / a mí / doler / después de / me / los pies / correr

_____

4. al Sr. Mirabal / interesar / americano / le / el fútbol

_____

5. los programas / les / a mis padres / de entrevistas / aburrir

_____

6. importar / voluntario / a nosotros / el trabajo / nos

_____

7. a Uds. / los boletos para el cine / les / para comprar / faltar / el dinero

_____

8. interesar / les / a José y a Felipe / policíacas / las películas

_____

9. el trabajo / a Angélica / aburrir / le

_____

10. la comida / italiana / encantar / a Vanessa y a mí / nos

_____

Realidades **B**

Capítulo 9A

Nombre _____

Hora _____

Fecha _____

Practice Workbook **9A–8**

Repaso

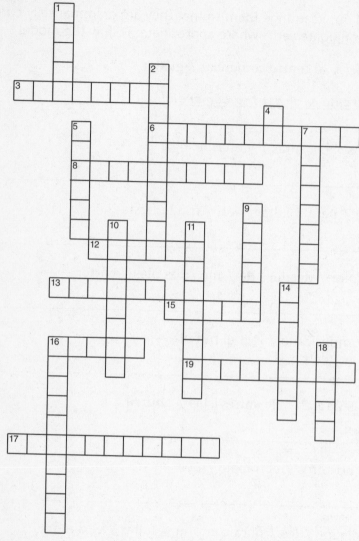

Down

1. Yo veo mis programas favoritos en el ____ cinco.
2. Es más que interesante; es ____.
4. *already*
5. No es actor, es ____.
7. No es interesante, es ____.
9. Me van a ____ zapatos. Necesito comprarlos.
10. Puedes leer las ____ o verlas en la tele.

11. película ____
14. *really?*
16. A Paco le gusta el fútbol. Ve programas ____.
18. No sé mucho ____ eso.

Across

3. Cuando vas al cine, ves una ____.

6.

8. un programa en la tele que cuenta las historias románticas de la gente; la ____

12. *therefore*
13. Una comedia es ____.
15. No es actriz, es ____.
16. Los programas ____ una hora.
17. *Entre tú y yo* es un programa de ____.
19. Cuando la gente gana dinero, es un programa de ____.

80 *Repaso del capítulo* ▬ *Crucigrama*

Realidades B

Capítulo 9A

Nombre _____

Fecha _____

Hora _____

Practice Workbook **9A–9**

Organizer

I. Vocabulary

Types of television programs	Types of movies
_____	_____
_____	_____
_____	_____
_____	_____
_____	_____
_____	_____
_____	_____

Words to describe movies/programs	Words to express opinions
_____	_____
_____	_____
_____	_____
_____	_____
_____	

II. Grammar

1. Use _____ + _____ to say what you or others have just finished doing.

2. **Me gusta** is literally translated as "_____". So, the construction is formed by putting the _____ first, followed by the _____, and finally the _____.

Realidades Ⓑ

Capítulo 9B

Nombre _____

Hora _____

Fecha _____

Practice Workbook **9B–1**

El laboratorio

Label the computer lab below with the appropriate words.

1. _____

2. _____

3. _____

4. _____

5. _____

6. _____

Go Online WEB CODE jcd-0911
PHSchool.com

Las asociaciones

Write the words from your vocabulary that you associate with each of the following definitions.

1. Una sala de clases con muchas computadoras _____

2. Lugar para hablar con otras personas en línea _____

3. Comunicarse con otros por computadora _____

4. Lo que haces si quieres aprender más _____

5. Buscar información _____

6. Un lugar de la Red dedicado a algún tema _____

7. Hacer actividades electrónicas divertidas _____

8. Una comunicación *no* por correo electrónico _____

9. Una carta que envías para una fecha especial _____

10. Expresar y comprender ideas de otra persona _____

11. Si quieres hacer un disco compacto _____

12. Un artista puede hacerlos en la computadora _____

El sitio Web

Sara has just purchased a laptop computer. She is so excited that she just has to tell her friend Ramón. In the e-mail below write the words that best complete her thoughts.

Ramón,

    Ay, amigo, tienes que comprarte una computadora

_____. ¡Son los mejores juguetes del mundo!

Cuando vas de vacaciones puedes llevarla en tu mochila y

cuando estás en el hotel puedes _____ en la

Red, escribir por _____ o

_____ información de la Red. ¿Y quieres

sacar fotos? Con una cámara _____ puedes

sacarlas y ponerlas en la computadora. También puedes

mandar las fotos a otra _____ electrónica

si quieres. ¿Qué te _____? ¿Es difícil?

Puedes _____ un curso para aprender más

sobre cómo usar esta clase de cámara y cómo crear

_____ en la computadora. No debes tener

_____ de buscar información sobre

cámaras digitales porque hay muchas personas que

_____ usarlas o que escribieron unos

_____ sobre estas cámaras.

    Bueno, podemos hablar más de esto _____

porque no tengo tiempo ahora. Hasta luego.

Sara

Go Online WEB CODE jcd-0912
PHSchool.com

¡Una computadora muy buena!

Your local newspaper recently ran an ad for a new computer and many of your friends bought one. Read some of the computer's capabilities in the ad below. Then, based on the information you are given about each person that bought this computer, say what he or she uses the new computer for. Follow the model.

CON LA COMPUTADORA ES POSIBLE:

- Grabar un disco compacto
- Preparar presentaciones
- Escribir por correo electrónico
- Usar una cámara digital
- Visitar salones de chat
- Navegar en la Red
- Crear documentos
- Estar en línea

Modelo A Juan le gusta bajar información.

Juan usa la computadora para estar en línea.

1. A Alejandro le gusta escribir cuentos y composiciones.

   _____

2. A Diego le gusta sacar fotos.

   _____

3. A Caridad le gusta tocar y escuchar música.

   _____

4. A Ramiro le gusta buscar los sitios Web.

   _____

5. A Esperanza le gusta conocer y hablar con otras personas.

   _____

6. A Lucita le gusta escribir tarjetas y cartas a su familia que vive en otra ciudad.

   _____

7. A Rodrigo le gusta enseñar a los niños.

   _____

Realidades B

Capítulo 9B

Nombre _____

Hora _____

Fecha _____

Practice Workbook **9B–5**

¿Pedir o servir?

A. Fill in the charts below with the present tense forms of the verbs **pedir** and **servir**.

	PEDIR	SERVIR
yo	pido	
tú		
él, ella, Ud.		sirve
nosotros		
vosotros	pedís	servís
ellos, ellas, Uds.		

B. Complete the mini-conversations below with the correct forms of **pedir** or **servir**.

1. —Cuando vas al restaurante Marino para comer, ¿qué _____ tú?

   —Normalmente _____ una ensalada y una pasta.

2. —¿Para qué _____ esto?

   —_____ para grabar discos compactos, hijo.

3. —¿Los camareros les _____ rápidamente en el restaurante Guzmán?

   —Sí, son muy trabajadores.

4. —No puedo ver esos gráficos.

   —(Nosotros) _____ ayuda, entonces.

5. —Bienvenida a la fiesta. ¿Le _____ algo?

   —Sí, un refresco, por favor.

6. —Vamos al restaurante. Esta noche ellos _____ pollo con salsa y pasta.

   —Yo siempre _____ el pollo.

7. —¿Para qué _____ el menú?

   —_____ para conocer la comida del restaurante. ¿Y qué vas a

   _____ del menú?

   —Yo siempre _____ la misma cosa. . . el bistec.

Go Online WEB CODE jcd-0913
PHSchool.com

Realidades B

Capítulo 9B

Nombre _____

Fecha _____

Hora _____

Practice Workbook **9B–6**

¿Saber o conocer?

A. Write either **saber** or **conocer** in the blanks under the items below.

1. Mi número de teléfono

   _____

2. Usar una computadora

   _____

3. El profesor de la clase de español

   _____

4. La película *Casablanca*

   _____

5. Leer música

6. La ciudad de Nueva York

   _____

7. Mi madre

   _____

8. Tu mejor amigo

   _____

9. Navegar en la Red

   _____

10. El sitio Web

   _____

B. Fill in the missing forms of **saber** and **conocer** in the charts below.

	SABER	CONOCER
yo		
tú		
él, ella, Ud.	*sabe*	*conoce*
nosotros		
vosotros	*sabéis*	*conocéis*
ellos, ellas, Uds.		

C. Complete the following sentences using the correct forms of **saber** or **conocer**.

1. Juan, ¿ _____ la fecha de hoy?

2. ¿Alguien _____ a un médico bueno?

3. Mis padres _____ bailar muy bien.

4. Nosotros _____ todas las palabras de la obra.

5. ¿ _____ dónde está el Museo del Prado?

Realidades B

Capítulo 9B

Nombre _____

Hora _____

Fecha _____

Practice Workbook **9B–7**

Planes para la noche

The Miranda family is planning to go out to eat. Fill in their conversation using forms of **conocer**, **saber**, **pedir**, or **servir**.

PADRE: Vamos al restaurante Vista del Mar. ¿Lo _____ Uds.? Me gusta

mucho.

TERESA: Yo no lo _____ pero _____ dónde está. ¡Quiero ir

a ese restaurante!

TOMÁS: Por supuesto que _____ dónde está, Tere, el nombre es Vista del Mar.

TERESA: Sí. ¿_____ Uds. que tienen el mejor pescado de la ciudad?

Es muy sabroso.

MADRE: ¿Y ellos _____ otra comida también?

TERESA: Yo no _____. ¿Sabes tú, Tomás?

TOMÁS: Sí. Allí _____ mucha comida rica.

PADRE: Yo _____ el pescado porque me encanta.

TOMÁS: Sí, me encanta el pescado también.

TERESA: Es verdad Tomás, pero siempre _____ la misma cosa cuando

comemos pescado.

PADRE: Por eso vamos a este restaurante. Puedes _____ de todo y va a ser

sabrosísimo.

TERESA: ¡Yo quiero _____ ese restaurante!

MADRE: Pues, estamos de acuerdo. Vamos a Vista del Mar.

Go Online WEB CODE jcd-0915
PHSchool.com

Realidades B

Capítulo 9B

Nombre _____

Fecha _____

Hora _____

Practice Workbook **9B–8**

Repaso

Down

1.
2. El cliente ___ un té helado porque tiene calor.
3. Voy a visitar Nueva York porque quiero ___ la.
4. ___ un disco compacto
6. Los estudiantes hacen un ___ del presidente Lincoln.
8. Quiero escribirte una carta. ¿Cuál es tu ___ electrónica?
9. Yo escribo por ___ electrónico.
11. Estoy en línea. Quiero ___ en ___ ___.
12. *song;* la ___
13. El ___ Web para este libro es *PHSchool.com.*
14. No tengo ese programa. Lo voy a ___ de la Red.
16. Necesito ___ información para mi informe.
18. La artista sabe muy bien hacer ___ en la computadora.
19. Necesito una computadora que puede ___ documentos.
21. *slide;* la ___

Across

1. Quiero ___ un curso.
5. No debes tener ___ de la tecnología.
7. Para navegar en la Red, hay que estar ___ ___.
10. Si quieres hablar con personas inmediata-mente, vas a un ___ de chat.
13. ¿Para qué ___?
15. *to communicate (with)*
17. Mi amiga me escribió una ___.
20. No me gusta hablar por teléfono. Me gusta hablar ___ ___ ___.

22. Voy a la escuela porque quiero ___ cómo hacer cosas.
23. Vamos al ___ para usar las computa-doras de la escuela.

24. la computadora ___

Organizer

I. Vocabulary

Words to talk about the Web

_____

_____

_____

_____

Words to name other electronics

_____

_____

_____

_____

Verbs related to online activities

_____

_____

_____

_____

_____

_____

II. Grammar

1. The present tense of **pedir** is:

_____ _____

_____ _____

_____ _____

The present tense of **servir** is:

_____ _____

_____ _____

_____ _____

2. Use the verb _____ for information or activities that you know. Use

the verb _____ to talk about familiarity with people, places, or things.

Go Online WEB CODE jcd-0916
PHSchool.com

Writing, Audio & Video Activities

Nombre _____ Hora _____

Fecha _____

VIDEO

Antes de ver el video

Actividad 1

Look at this family tree. Label each person with his or her relationship to Ricardo.

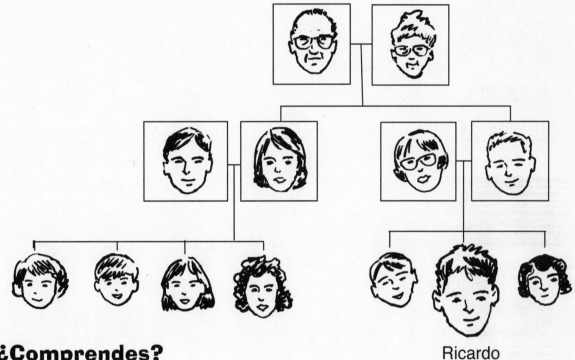

Ricardo

¿Comprendes?

Actividad 2

Cristina had a birthday party with some of her family members. How much do you remember about that party? Write **cierto** or **falso** next to each statement.

1. Angélica hace un video de la fiesta de su hermano. _____

2. El papá de Cristina saca fotos de la fiesta. _____

3. A Gabriel le gustan los deportes. _____

4. El perro de Cristina se llama Piñata. _____

5. La abuela de Cristina decora la fiesta con papel picado. _____

6. Capitán es muy sociable, le encanta estar con la familia. _____

7. Carolina es la hermana de Gabriel y Angélica. _____

8. Ricardo es el abuelo de Esteban. _____

Nombre _____ Hora _____

Fecha _____

VIDEO

Actividad 3

Who is being described? Write his or her name next to the description.

	Description	Name

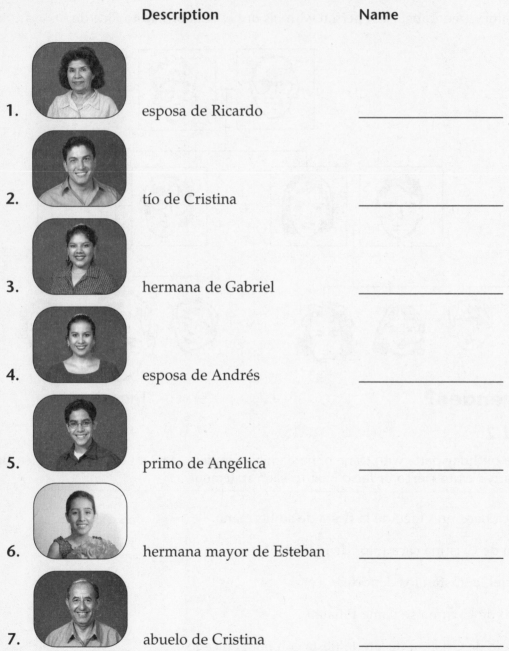

1. esposa de Ricardo _____

2. tío de Cristina _____

3. hermana de Gabriel _____

4. esposa de Andrés _____

5. primo de Angélica _____

6. hermana mayor de Esteban _____

7. abuelo de Cristina _____

Y, ¿qué más?

Actividad 4

At Cristina's party we met many family members. Why don't you introduce your family, too? Write three sentences about your family or a family you know well. Follow the examples below.

Yo vivo en mi casa con mi mamá y mi hermano.

TÚ: _____

Mi hermano se llama Martín y tiene 10 años.

TÚ: _____

Yo tengo muchos primos y primas.

TÚ: _____

The lyrics for "Las mañanitas" as sung on the video are:

Éstas son las mañanitas que cantaba el rey David
a las muchachas bonitas, te las cantamos a ti.
Despierta, mi bien, despierta, mira que ya amaneció,
ya los pajarillos cantan, la luna ya se metió.

These are the early morning birthday songs
that King David used to sing
to pretty girls, and so we sing them to you.
Wake up, my dear, wake up, look, dawn has already come,
the little birds are singing, the moon is gone.

Nombre _____   Hora _____

Fecha _____

Actividad 5

Beto is showing Raúl a picture of his family at a birthday party. Identify as many people as you can and write their names and relationship to Beto under the pictures. If Beto refers to a pet, simply write the pet's name under the picture. You will hear this conversation twice.

_____   _____   _____

_____   _____   _____

_____   _____   _____

_____   _____   _____

_____   _____   _____

_____   _____   _____

Nombre _____   Hora _____

Fecha _____   **AUDIO**

Actividad 6

You are chosen to participate in a popular radio quiz show on a local Spanish radio station. When it is your turn, you are happy to hear that your questions are in the category of **FAMILIA**. See if you can answer all of the questions correctly on the entry card below. Each question becomes a little more difficult. You will hear each set of questions twice.

1. _____

2. _____

3. _____

4. _____

5. _____

Actividad 7

Listen as three brothers talk to their mother after school. Try to fill in all of the squares in the grid with the correct information about Julio, Mateo, and Víctor. Remember, you might not hear the information given in the same order as it appears in the grid. You will hear this conversation twice.

	¿Cuántos años tiene?	¿Qué le gusta hacer?	¿Qué tiene que hacer?	¿Qué tiene en la mochila?
Julio				
Mateo				
Víctor				

Nombre _____ Hora _____

Fecha _____

Actividad 8

Listen as two students tell their host families in Chile about their own families back home. As you listen to both of them, see if you can tell which family is being described. Put a check mark in the appropriate box on the grid. You will hear each set of statements twice.

La familia Gómez

La familia Sora

	1	2	3	4	5	6	7	8
La familia Gómez								
La familia Sora								

Realidades **B**

Capítulo 5A

Nombre _____

Fecha _____

Hora _____

AUDIO

Actividad 9

Listen to the following phone calls to Ana, a favorite local talk show host. Each caller has a problem with someone in his or her family. As you listen to each caller, take notes on his or her problems. After all of the callers have spoken, write a sentence of advice for each caller. You may write your advice in English. You will hear set of statements twice.

	PROBLEMA	CONSEJO
Maritza		
Armando		
Andrés		
María Luisa		

Nombre _____

Hora _____

Fecha _____

Actividad 10

Look at the pages from the Rulfo family photo album below. Then, write one or two sentences describing the people in each photo. What is their relationship to each other? What do you think they are like, based on the pictures?

Juanito, Lolita y Pepe

Pepe, Marcos, Romana, Timoteo y Luisita

"El cumpleaños de Rafael"

1. Foto 1

_____

_____

_____

2. Foto 2

_____

_____

_____

3. Foto 3

_____

_____

_____

Realidades **B**

Capítulo 5A

Nombre _____

Fecha _____

Hora _____

WRITING

Actividad 11

People have many obligations during the day. Using **tener que**, write what you think the following people have to do at the time of day or place given. Follow the model.

Modelo   mi padre / a las 7:00 de la mañana

Mi padre tiene que desayunar a las siete de la mañana.

1. yo / a las 7:30 de la mañana

   _____

2. tú / en la clase de español

   _____

3. los estudiantes / en la clase de inglés

   _____

4. el profesor / en la clase de matemáticas

   _____

5. las personas de la escuela / a las doce de la tarde (al mediodía)

   _____

6. Uds. / en la clase de arte

   _____

7. los estudiantes malos / en la clase de educación física

   _____

8. mi amigo / a las 3:00 de la tarde

   _____

9. mis hermanos y yo / a las 5:00 de la tarde

   _____

10. mi familia / a las 6:00 de la tarde

    _____

Nombre _____

Hora _____

Fecha _____

WRITING

Actividad 12

A. Your family tree is very complex. It takes many links to connect everyone in the family. Using possessive adjectives, write 10 sentences about how people are related in your family. Use the model to help you.

Modelo   *Mi tío tiene dos hijos.*

   Mi abuelo es el padre de mi tía.

1. _____

2. _____

3. _____

4. _____

5. _____

6. _____

7. _____

8. _____

9. _____

10. _____

B. Now, draw your family tree.

Realidades **B**

Capítulo 5A

Nombre _____

Hora _____

Fecha _____

WRITING

Actividad 13

Your pen pal from Argentina has asked you to tell her about a member of your family. First, tell her the person's name, age, and relationship to you. Then, describe what the person is like.

Once you finish writing, read your description and check to make sure that all the words are spelled correctly and that you have used accents where necessary. Also, check to make sure the endings of the adjectives agree with the nouns they are describing.

Hola, Ana Sofía:

_____

_____

_____

_____

_____

_____

_____

_____

_____

_____

Saludos,

_____

Realidades B

Capítulo 5B

Nombre _____

Hora _____

Fecha _____

VIDEO

Antes de ver el video

Actividad 1

Select from the word bank the appropriate nouns to write under each heading: things needed to set the table, things to eat, and things to drink.

menú	tacos	tenedor	flan
enchiladas	limonada	servilleta	postre
café	refresco	cuchillo	jugo de naranja

Para poner la mesa

_____

_____

_____

Para comer

_____

_____

_____

Para beber

_____

_____

_____

¿Comprendes?

Actividad 2

Angélica's family is having dinner at the restaurant **México Lindo**. Find the best choice to complete each statement by writing the letter in the space provided.

1. El camarero está nervioso; _____
   a. tiene mucho trabajo.
   b. es su primer día de trabajo.
   c. tiene sueño.

2. El papá de Angélica pide un té helado _____
   a. porque tiene calor.
   b. porque es delicioso.
   c. porque tiene frío.

Realidades **B**

Capítulo 5B

Nombre

Hora

Fecha

VIDEO

3. La mamá de Angélica pide de postre _____

   a. arroz con pollo.

   b. tacos de bistec.

   c. flan.

4. La mamá de Angélica necesita _____

   a. una servilleta.

   b. el menú.

   c. un cuchillo y un tenedor.

Actividad 3

Match each person with the things he or she ordered. Write the letter of the foods and beverages in the spaces provided.

1. Mamá _____

a. jugo de naranja y fajitas de pollo

2. Angélica _____

b. enchiladas

3. Papá _____

c. café, ensalada de frutas y flan

4. Esteban _____

d. té helado, tacos de bistec y café

5. Cristina _____

e. refresco y arroz con pollo

6. Sr. del pelo castaño _____

f. hamburguesa y refresco

Nombre _____   Hora _____

Fecha _____

VIDEO

Y, ¿qué más?

Actividad 4

You and your friend Graciela are having dinner at a Mexican restaurant with your family. Graciela doesn't speak Spanish, so your mom orders dinner for her. Then, you give your order. Look at the menu to see your options, then write your order in the space provided in the dialogue below.

MENÚ		
BEBIDAS	**PLATO PRINCIPAL**	**POSTRES**
Refrescos	Enchiladas	Flan
Jugo de naranja	Tacos de carne/pollo	Helado
Té helado/caliente	Fajitas de carne/pollo	Frutas frescas
Café	Burritos	

CAMARERO: ¿Qué van a pedir para beber?

MAMÁ: La joven quiere un jugo de naranja, y yo quiero un refresco.

TÚ: _____

CAMARERO: ¿Qué quieren pedir para el plato principal?

MAMÁ: Para la joven enchiladas, y yo quiero arroz con pollo.

TÚ: _____

CAMARERO: ¿Quieren pedir algo de postre?

MAMÁ: Para la joven un flan. Yo no quiero nada, gracias.

TÚ: _____

Nombre _____

Hora _____

Fecha _____

Actividad 5

You are delighted to find out that you can understand a conversation that a family at a table near you in a restaurant is having in Spanish. The family doesn't seem very happy with the waiter. Listen to find out what each family member is upset about. By looking at the pictures in the grid below, check off the item that is causing the problem. You will hear each conversation twice.

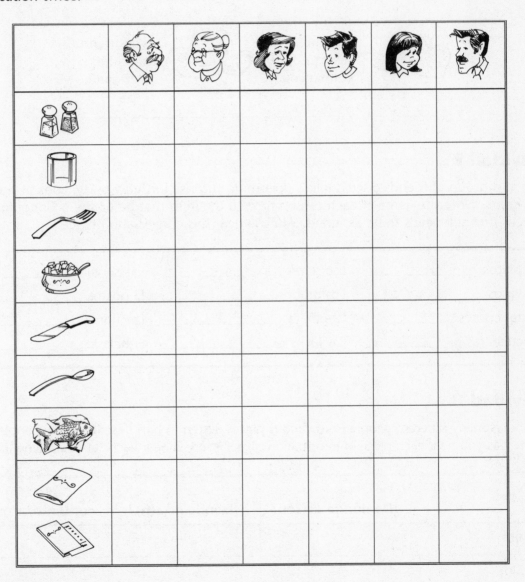

Actividad 6

Five young people go to a department store to buy hats (**sombreros**) as presents for their friends. Listen as each person describes the person he or she is buying the present for. Write the name of each person described under the hat that best matches that person. You will hear each conversation twice.

sociable, deportista, atrevido(a)

romántico(a), talentoso(a), paciente

serio(a), trabajador(a), práctico(a)

_____

_____

_____

elegante, divertido(a), simpático(a)

aventurero(a), atrevido(a), interesante

_____

_____

Actividad 7

Listen as a group of friends discuss Julia's upcoming surprise birthday party. Look at the list of party items. Write the name of each person next to the item that he or she is bringing. Circle any item that still needs to be assigned. You will hear this conversation twice.

Los platos _____	Los refrescos _____	Las servilletas _____
Los vasos _____	Los globos _____	El postre _____
Los tenedores _____	La piñata _____	Las flores _____
Las cucharas _____	Las luces _____	El helado _____

Actividad 8

Iván knows many different people from various places. Listen to him describe these people. Fill in the chart as you hear each piece of information given. You will hear each set of statements twice.

	¿De dónde es/son?	¿Dónde está(n)?	¿Está(n) contento/a/os/as?
Juanita			
Los tíos			
Iván y su familia			
Felipe			
Juanita y Julie			

Realidades **B**

Capítulo 5B

Nombre _____

Hora _____

Fecha _____

AUDIO

Actividad 9

Listen as a girl describes a photo of a party to her friend who was unable to attend. Write the names of each person described on the line that corresponds to each picture. You will hear the dialogues twice.

A. _____   D. _____

B. _____   E. _____

C. _____   F. _____

WRITING

Actividad 10

Draw a picture of yourself and three other people in your family. Then, write a description of the person below each picture. You can draw imaginary family members if you prefer.

1.

_____ Yo _____

_____

_____

_____

_____

_____

2.

_____

_____

_____

_____

_____

_____

3.

_____

_____

_____

_____

_____

_____

4.

_____

_____

_____

_____

_____

_____

Realidades B

Capítulo 5B

Nombre _____

Fecha _____

Hora _____

WRITING

Actividad 11

In preparation for their upcoming party, Juan and Elisa are talking on the phone about who is coming and what each guest is bringing. Read Elisa's guest list below, then complete the friends' conversation by writing sentences that include the correct form of either **venir** or **traer**.

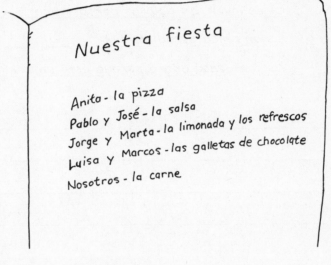

Nuestra fiesta

Anita - la pizza
Pablo y José - la salsa
Jorge y Marta - la limonada y los refrescos
Luisa y Marcos - las galletas de chocolate
Nosotros - la carne

JUAN: ¿Anita viene a la fiesta el sábado?

ELISA: _____.

JUAN: ¡Qué bien! ¿También van a venir Pablo y José?

ELISA: Sí. Ellos _____

JUAN: ¿Qué traen ellos?

ELISA: _____.

JUAN: Bien. Y ¿quién trae las bebidas?

ELISA: Pues, _____.

JUAN: Sí. Ahora, ¿quiénes traen el postre?

ELISA: _____.

JUAN: ¡Perfecto! ¿Y nosotros? ¿_____?

ELISA: ¡Traemos la carne, por supuesto!

Nombre _____   Hora _____

Fecha _____   **WRITING**

Actividad 12

Describe the following people. Consider their mood and location, their personality and appearance. Be creative and use the pictures and model to help you.

Modelo

Él es joven. Su pelo es corto y negro.

Es un chico estudioso.

Está en casa ahora porque está enfermo.

1. _____
_____
_____
_____

2. _____
_____
_____
_____

3. _____
_____
_____
_____

4. _____
_____
_____
_____

Realidades B

Capítulo 5B

Nombre _____

Fecha _____

Hora _____

WRITING

Actividad 13

There is going to be a picnic at your new house, and your mother is telling you who is coming and what he or she will be bringing. Write what your mother says, using a name, a description word, and an item from the columns below. Use either **venir** or **traer** in your sentence. Use the names only once. Follow the model.

Nombre	Descripción	Va a traer
Los Sres. Vázquez	viejo	platos
	joven	tenedores
La Srta. Espinosa	contento	vasos
	simpático	pollo
Antonio Jerez	artístico	hamburguesas
	pelirrojo	pasteles
Fernando y María Sosa	enfermo	servilletas
	guapo	limonada
Catalina de la Cuesta	alto	cuchillos
	bajo	tazas

Modelo *La señorita Espinosa viene a la fiesta. Ella es la mujer joven y simpática que vive cerca de nuestra casa. Ella siempre está contenta y trae los pasteles.*

1. _____

_____

2. _____

_____

3. _____

_____

4. _____

_____

Nombre _____ Hora _____

Fecha _____

VIDEO

Antes de ver el video

Actividad 1

Make a list of five items in your bedroom and five adjectives that describe your bedroom.

Cosas en mi dormitorio

_____

_____

_____

_____

_____

Descripción de mi dormitorio

_____

_____

_____

_____

_____

¿Comprendes?

Actividad 2

Below are some words and phrases that you have learned so far. On the lines below, write only the words that you most likely heard in the video episode about Ignacio's room.

a veces	ratón	bistec	¿A qué hora?	almuerzo
foto	desordenado	lámpara	pequeños	estante
pared	bueno	casa	mochila	peor
abuelos	bailar	cuarto	bicicleta	escritorio
calculadora	¿Adónde?	fiesta	discos compactos	color

_____ _____ _____

_____ _____ _____

_____ _____ _____

_____ _____ _____

Actividad 3

Put the following scenes from the video in chronological order by numbering them from 1–7.

Realidades **B**

Capítulo 6A

Nombre _____

Fecha _____

Hora _____

VIDEO

Y, ¿qué más?

Actividad 4

What is your room like? Is it messy or neat? What do you have to the left and to the right of the room? What do you have on the wall, on the nightstand, or on a bookshelf? Can you compare your room to someone else's? Describe your room, using as much new vocabulary as you can. Follow the sample paragraph below.

Modelo

Mi cuarto es menos ordenado que el cuarto de mi hermana. A la izquierda tengo un estante, muy desordenado, con discos compactos. A la derecha está mi escritorio con libros y revistas. Tengo una foto de mi familia en la pared. También tengo otra foto de mi hermana en su cuarto, ¡ y está ordenado!

_____

_____

_____

_____

_____

_____

_____

Realidades **B**

Capítulo 6A

Nombre _____

Fecha _____

Hora _____

AUDIO

Actividad 5

Marta and her sister Ana have very similar bedrooms. However, since they have unique personalities and tastes, there are some differences! For each statement you hear, check off in the appropriate column whose bedroom is being described. You will hear each statement twice.

El dormitorio de Marta

El dormitorio de Ana

	Marta	Ana			Marta	Ana
1.	❑	❑		6.	❑	❑
2.	❑	❑		7.	❑	❑
3.	❑	❑		8.	❑	❑
4.	❑	❑		9.	❑	❑
5.	❑	❑		10.	❑	❑

Realidades Ⓑ

Capítulo 6A

Nombre

Fecha

Hora

AUDIO

Actividad 6

Your Spanish teacher asks you to represent your school at a local university's **Competencia Escolar** (*Scholastic Competition*) for secondary Spanish students. She gives you a tape to practice with for the competition. As you listen to the recording, decide whether the statement is true or false and mark it in the grid. You will hear each set of statements twice.

	1	2	3	4	5	6	7	8	9	10
Cierto										
Falso										

Actividad 7

Sra. Harding's class is planning an Immersion Weekend for the school district's Spanish students. Listen as four committee members discuss the best food to have, the best activities for younger and older students, and the best colors for the t-shirt (**camiseta**) that will be given to all participants. To keep track of what everyone thinks, fill in the grid. You will hear each set of statements twice.

	La mejor comida	Las actividades para los estudiantes menores	Las actividades para los estudiantes mayores	El mejor color para la camiseta
1				
2				
3				
4				

Nombre _____

Hora _____

Fecha _____

Actividad 8

Your friend is babysitting for a family with an eight-year-old boy and a ten-year-old girl. Since they are a Spanish-speaking family, your friend wants you to go with her in case she doesn't understand everything that the mother tells her. Listen to the conversation to learn all the ground rules. Write either **sí** or **no** in each column that matches what the mother says that the boy or girl can do. Be sure to write **no** in both columns if neither is allowed to do it. Write **sí** in both columns if both are allowed to do it. You will hear this conversation twice.

Realidades B

Capítulo 6A

Nombre _____

Hora _____

Fecha _____

AUDIO

Actividad 9

Look at the pictures in the chart below as you hear people describe their friends' bedrooms. Place a check in the chart that corresponds to all of the items mentioned by the friend. You will hear each set of statements twice.

	Javier	Sara	María	Marcos

Nombre _____   Hora _____

Fecha _____   **WRITING**

Actividad 10

Answer the following questions about your bedroom in complete sentences. If you prefer, you may write about your ideal bedroom.

1. ¿Cuál es tu color favorito?

_____

2. ¿De qué color es tu dormitorio?

_____

3. ¿Tienes una alfombra en tu dormitorio? ¿De qué color es?

_____

4. ¿Tienes un despertador? ¿Cuándo usas tu despertador?

_____

_____

5. ¿Qué muebles (*furniture*) tienes en tu dormitorio?

_____

_____

6. ¿Qué cosas electrónicas tienes en tu dormitorio?

_____

7. ¿Prefieres los videos o los DVDs? ¿Cuántos tienes?

_____

8. ¿Cuántos discos compactos tienes?

_____

Nombre _____

Hora _____

Fecha _____

WRITING

Actividad 11

A. Draw your bedroom or your ideal bedroom (including furniture, electronics, windows, books, decorations, and other possessions) in the space provided below.

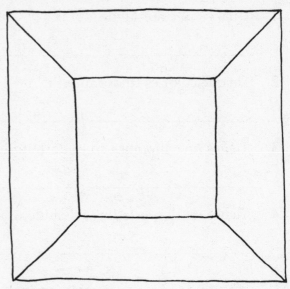

B. Now, compare the room that you drew with Juan's room on the left. Use the correct form of some of the following adjectives, or think of others: **práctico**, **interesante**, **grande**, **pequeño**, **mejor**, **peor**, **bonito**, **ordenado**.

| Modelo | *Mi dormitorio es menos interesante que el dormitorio de Juan.* |

1. _____

2. _____

3. _____

4. _____

5. _____

6. _____

Realidades B

Capítulo 6A

Nombre _____

Hora _____

Fecha _____

WRITING

Actividad 12

You and your friends are comparing your English classes to determine which teacher's class to take next year. Read the information below, then compare the classes based on the criteria indicated. Follow the model.

	Clase A	Clase B	Clase C
Hora	Primera	Tercera	Octava
Profesor(a)	Profesora Brown — interesante	Profesor Martí — aburrido	Profesor Nicólas — muy interesante
Número de estudiantes	25	20	22
Dificultad	Difícil	Muy difícil	Fácil
Libros	Muy buenos	Aburridos	Buenos
Opinión general	A	B–	A–

Modelo Profesor _El profesor Martí es el menos interesante de los tres profesores._

1. Hora (*temprano* or *tarde*)

   _____

2. Número de estudiantes (*grande* or *pequeña*)

   _____

3. Dificultad (*fácil* or *difícil*)

   _____

4. Libros (*buenos* or *malos*)

   _____

5. Opinión general (*mejor* or *peor*)

   _____

Realidades **B**

Capítulo 6A

Nombre _____

Hora _____

Fecha _____

WRITING

Actividad 13

Your parents are hosting a family reunion, and nine extra people will be sleeping at your house. On the lines below, write where nine guests would sleep at your house. You may use your imagination if you prefer.

1. _____

_____

2. _____

_____

3. _____

_____

4. _____

_____

5. _____

_____

6. _____

_____

7. _____

_____

8. _____

_____

9. _____

_____

Antes de ver el video

Actividad 1

Think of five chores you do at home. Then, write whether you like or don't like doing them using **me gusta** and **no me gusta nada**. Follow the model.

Modelo *No me gusta nada limpiar mi dormitorio.* _____

1. _____
2. _____
3. _____
4. _____
5. _____

¿Comprendes?

Actividad 2

As you know from the video, Jorgito does all of the chores even though some were Elena's responsibility. Next to each chore listed below, tell whether it was Elena's responsibility or Jorgito's responsibility by writing the appropriate name in the space provided.

1. _____ quitar el polvo
2. _____ poner la mesa del comedor
3. _____ lavar los platos en la cocina
4. _____ hacer la cama en el dormitorio de Jorge
5. _____ hacer la cama en el cuarto de Elena
6. _____ arreglar el dormitorio de Jorge
7. _____ pasar la aspiradora
8. _____ dar de comer al perro

Actividad 3

Use the stills below from the video to help you answer the questions. Use complete sentences.

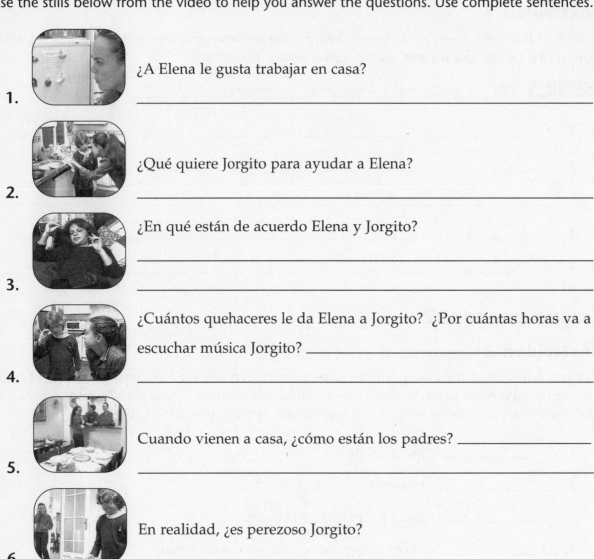

1. ¿A Elena le gusta trabajar en casa?

   _____

2. ¿Qué quiere Jorgito para ayudar a Elena?

   _____

3. ¿En qué están de acuerdo Elena y Jorgito?

   _____

   _____

4. ¿Cuántos quehaceres le da Elena a Jorgito? ¿Por cuántas horas va a

   escuchar música Jorgito? _____

   _____

5. Cuando vienen a casa, ¿cómo están los padres? _____

   _____

6. En realidad, ¿es perezoso Jorgito?

   _____

Y, ¿qué más?

Actividad 4

What activities might you do in each of these rooms? From the list in the box below, name at least two things that you might logically do in each room. Each activity should be used only once.

hacer la cama	pasar la aspiradora	escuchar música	cocinar la comida
	poner la mesa	lavar los platos	quitar el polvo
comer la cena	arreglar el dormitorio desordenado		hacer la tarea

1. dormitorio de Elena

_____   _____

2. sala

_____   _____

3. comedor

_____   _____

4. cocina

_____   _____

5. dormitorio de Jorge

_____   _____

Realidades Ⓑ

Capítulo 6B

Nombre _____

Hora _____

Fecha _____

AUDIO

Actividad 5

Listen as people look for things they have misplaced somewhere in their house. After each conversation, complete the sentence that explains what each person is looking for (**busca**) and in which room it is found. You will hear each dialogue twice.

1. La muchacha busca _____.

   Está en _____.

2. El muchacho busca _____.

   Está en _____.

3. La mujer busca _____.

   Está en _____.

4. El muchacho busca _____.

   Está en _____.

5. La muchacha busca _____.

   Está en _____.

Actividad 6

Señor Morales's nephew, Paco, volunteers to help his uncle move into a new apartment. However, Señor Morales is very distracted as he tells Paco where to put different things. Listen as he gives his nephew instructions and record in the grid below whether you think what he tells him to do each time is **lógico** (logical) **o ilógico** (illogical). You will hear each dialogue twice.

	1	2	3	4	5	6	7	8	9	10
lógico										
ilógico										

Nombre _____ Hora _____

Fecha _____

Actividad 7

Nico's parents are shocked when they come home from a trip to find that he hasn't done any of the chores that he promised to do. As they tell Nico what he needs to do, fill in the blanks below each picture with the corresponding number. You will hear each set of statements twice.

Actividad 8

Listen as each person rings a friend's doorbell and is told by the person who answers the door what the friend is doing at the moment. Based on that information, in which room of the house would you find the friend? As you listen to the conversations, look at the drawing of the house and write the number of the room that you think each friend might be in. You will hear each dialogue twice.

1. _____
2. _____
3. _____
4. _____
5. _____
6. _____

Realidades B

Capítulo 6B

Nombre _____

Hora _____

Fecha _____

AUDIO

Actividad 9

Some people always seem to get out of doing their chores at home. Listen as a few teens tell their parents why they should not or cannot do what their parents have asked them to do. As you listen, write in the chart below what the parent requests, such as **lavar los platos**. Then write in the teens' excuses, such as **está lavando el coche**. You will hear each conversation twice.

	Los quehaceres	Las excusas
Marcos		
Luis		
Marisol		
Jorge		
Elisa		

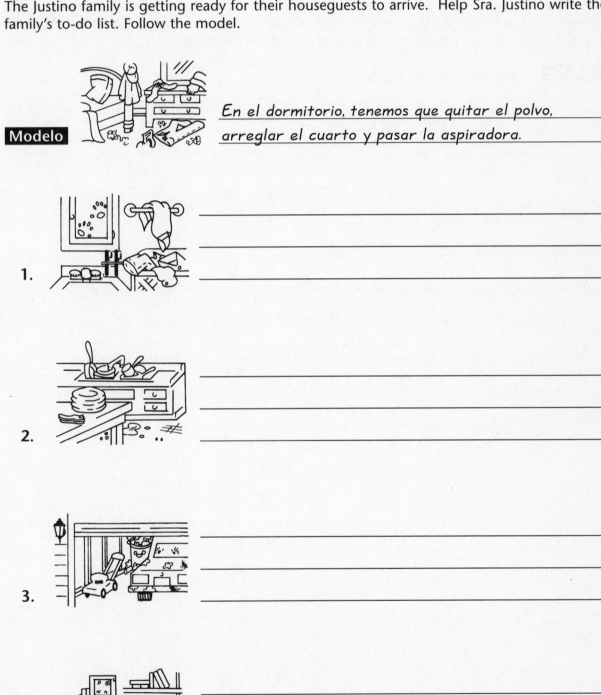

Realidades **B**

Capítulo 6B

Nombre _____

Hora _____

Fecha _____

WRITING

Actividad 10

The Justino family is getting ready for their houseguests to arrive. Help Sra. Justino write the family's to-do list. Follow the model.

Modelo

En el dormitorio, tenemos que quitar el polvo, arreglar el cuarto y pasar la aspiradora.

1. _____
   _____
   _____

2. _____
   _____
   _____

3. _____
   _____
   _____

4. _____
   _____
   _____

Nombre _____ Hora _____

Fecha _____

Actividad 11

The Boteros's son is going to stay with his grandmother in Puerto Rico for a month. His parents want to make sure that he is well-behaved and helps out around the house. Write ten commands the Boteros might give to their son. Follow the model.

Modelo   *Ayuda en la cocina, hijo.* _____

1. _____

2. _____

3. _____

4. _____

5. _____

6. _____

7. _____

8. _____

9. _____

10. _____

Nombre _____ Hora _____

Fecha _____

Actividad 12

The Galgo family is very busy on Sunday. Look at their schedule below and write what each family member is doing at the time given. Use your imagination, and use the model to help you.

	10:00	12:00	3:00	8:00
La Señora Galgo	hacer ejercicio	almorzar	trabajar	dormir
El Señor Galgo	trabajar	cortar el césped	preparar la cena	jugar al tenis
Rodrigo	arreglar el cuarto	comer	tocar la guitarra	estudiar
Mariana	nadar	poner la mesa	leer	ver la tele

Modelo   12:00   _A las doce, la Sra. Galgo está almorzando con sus amigos y el Sr._
Galgo está cortando el césped. Rodrigo está comiendo una manzana y
Mariana está poniendo la mesa.

1. 10:00

_____

_____

_____

_____

2. 3:00

_____

_____

_____

_____

3. 8:00

_____

_____

_____

_____

Realidades B

Capítulo 6B

Nombre _____

Hora _____

Fecha _____

WRITING

Actividad 13

A. Read the letter that Marta wrote to "Querida Adela," an advice column in the local paper, because she was frustrated with having to help around the house.

> Querida Adela:
>
> Yo soy una hija de 16 años y no tengo tiempo para ayudar en la casa. Mis padres no comprenden que yo tengo mi propia vida y que mis amigos son más importantes que los quehaceres de la casa. ¿Qué debo hacer?
>
> —Hija Malcontenta

B. Now, imagine that you are Adela and are writing a response to Marta. In the first paragraph, tell her what she must do around the house. In the second, tell her what she can do to still have fun with her friends. Use the sentences already below to help you.

Querida Hija Malcontenta:

Es verdad que tú tienes un problema. Piensas que tu vida con tus amigos es más importante que tu vida con tu familia. Pero, hija, tú tienes responsabilidades. Arregla tu cuarto. _____

_____

_____

_____

Tienes que ser una buena hija.

Después de ayudar a tus padres, llama a tus amigos por teléfono.

_____

_____

_____

_____. Tus padres van a estar más con-

tentos y tú vas a tener una vida mejor.

Buena suerte

Adela

Realidades **B**

Capítulo 7A

Nombre _____

Fecha _____

Hora _____

VIDEO

Antes de ver el video

Actividad 1

In the next video, Claudia and Teresa go shopping for clothes. In order to make decisions on what they want they will sometimes make comparisons. Using the following words, make a comparative statement for each set. Follow the model.

Modelo   blusa roja / blusa amarilla

La blusa roja es más bonita que la blusa amarilla.

1. botas marrones / botas negras

   _____

2. una falda larga / una mini falda

   _____

3. un traje nuevo / un traje de moda (*in fashion*)

   _____

4. Claudia – 16 años / Teresa – 15 años

   _____

5. suéter que cuesta 40 dólares / suéter que cuesta 30 dólares

   _____

¿Comprendes?

Actividad 2

Identify the speaker of the following quotes by writing the name of each person on the space provided.

1. "Tienes ropa muy bonita."   _____

2. "Quiero comprar algo nuevo."   _____

3.   "¿Qué tal esta tienda?"   _____

Realidades B

Capítulo 7A

Nombre _____

Fecha _____

Hora _____

VIDEO

4. "Pues entonces, ¿esta falda y esta blusa?" _____

5. "Busco algo bonito para una fiesta." _____

6. "Bueno, hay cosas que no cuestan tanto." _____

7. "Bueno, uhm, aquí en México no llevamos
   esa ropa en las fiestas." _____

8. "¡... pero es mi gorra favorita!" _____

Actividad 3

Can you remember what happened in the video? Write the letter of the correct answer on the line.

1. A Teresa no le gusta la falda y el vestido; _____

   a. le quedan bien.

   b. le quedan más o menos.

   c. le quedan mal.

2. A Teresa no le gusta su ropa, pero sí tiene ropa _____

   a. bonita.

   b. fea.

   c. muy vieja.

3. Teresa quiere _____

   a. comprar algo extravagante.

   b. comprar algo nuevo.

   c. no ir a la fiesta.

Realidades B

Capítulo 7A

Nombre _____

Fecha _____

Hora _____

VIDEO

4. Claudia quiere ver _____

  a. cuánto cuestan la falda y la blusa.

  b. si le quedan bien los jeans y la camiseta.

  c. otras cosas más bonitas.

5. Por fin las chicas deciden comprar _____

  a. unos jeans de cuatrocientos pesos con una camiseta de doscientos pesos.

  b. en otra tienda.

  c. una falda de trescientos pesos y un suéter de doscientos pesos.

Y, ¿qué más?

Actividad 4

Do you like the clothes that you have in your closet? Write one sentence about something in your closet that you do like, and why. Then write one sentence about something in your closet that you don't like, and why not. Follow the models.

Modelo 1   *Me gusta el suéter negro porque es bonito y puedo llevarlo*

cuando hace frío.

_____

_____

Modelo 2   *No me gustan los pantalones rojos porque son feos y me quedan mal.*

_____

_____

Nombre _____   Hora _____

Fecha _____

Actividad 5

Isabel is working at a laundry (**lavandería**) in Salamanca. As the customers bring in their order, write how many clothing items each person has from each category in the appropriate boxes. Then total the order and write the amount in the blanks provided in the grid for each customer. You will hear each dialogue twice.

LAVANDERÍA DOS PASOS
(Note: € is the symbol for Euros)

	Precios	Cliente 1	Cliente 2	Cliente 3	Cliente 4	Cliente 5
Blusas	3 €					
Vestidos	6 €					
Pantalones	8 €					
Faldas	5 €					
Suéteres	5 €					
Camisas	3 €					
Jeans	7 €					
Chaquetas	9 €					
Camisetas	3 €					
	TOTAL					

Actividad 6

Listen to the following items available from one of the shopping services on TV. You might not understand all of the words, but listen for the words that you do know in order to identify which item is being discussed. Then write down the price underneath the correct picture. You will hear each set of statements twice.

_____ _____ _____ _____ _____

Actividad 7

Listen as friends talk about their plans for the weekend. Where are they thinking about going? What are they thinking about doing? How are they planning to dress? As you listen for these details, fill in the chart. You will hear each dialogue twice.

	¿Adónde piensa ir?	¿Qué piensa hacer?	¿Qué piensa llevar?
1. Paco			
2. Anita			
3. Ernesto			
4. Kiki			

Actividad 8

Susi is spending the summer in Ecuador, where she is living with a wonderful host family. As the summer comes to a close, she is searching for the perfect thank-you gifts for each member of the family. Listen as she talks to the sales clerk. In the chart below, write in the item that she decides to buy for each person in her new "family." You will hear this conversation twice.

Para la madre	Para el padre	Para el hijo, Luis	Para la hija, Marisol	Para el bebé

Realidades B

Capítulo 7A

Nombre _____

Hora _____

Fecha _____

AUDIO

Actividad 9

What you wear can reveal secrets about your personality. Find out what type of message you send when you wear your favorite clothes and your favorite colors. As you listen to the descriptions, write down at least one word or phrase for each color personality and at least one article of clothing favored by that person. You will hear each set of statements twice.

EL COLOR	LA ROPA	LA PERSONALIDAD
Rojo		
Amarillo		
Morado		
Azul		
Anaranjado		
Marrón		
Gris		
Verde		
Negro		

Actividad 10

Answer the following questions about clothing and shopping in complete sentences.

1. ¿Quién va mucho de compras en tu familia?

_____

2. ¿Piensas comprar ropa nueva esta estación? ¿Qué piensas comprar?

_____

_____

3. ¿Cuál prefieres, la ropa del verano o la ropa del invierno? ¿Por qué?

_____

_____

4. ¿Prefieres la ropa de tus amigos o la ropa de tus padres? ¿Por qué?

_____

_____

5. ¿Prefieres llevar ropa formal o informal?

_____

6. ¿Qué llevas normalmente para ir a la escuela?

_____

_____

_____

7. ¿Cuál es tu ropa favorita? Describe.

_____

_____

_____

Nombre _____

Hora _____

Fecha _____

Actividad 11

Some students are thinking about what to wear for the next school dance. Look at the pictures, then write complete sentences telling what the students might be thinking. Use the verbs **pensar, querer,** or **preferir.** Follow the model.

Modelo

María piensa llevar un vestido negro al baile. También quiere llevar
unos zapatos negros. Quiere ser muy elegante.

1. _____

_____

_____

2. _____

_____

_____

3. _____

_____

_____

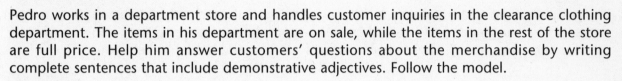

Actividad 12

Pedro works in a department store and handles customer inquiries in the clearance clothing department. The items in his department are on sale, while the items in the rest of the store are full price. Help him answer customers' questions about the merchandise by writing complete sentences that include demonstrative adjectives. Follow the model.

Modelo ¿Cuánto cuestan los suéteres?

Estos suéteres aquí cuestan cuarenta dólares y esos allí cuestan sesenta.

1. ¿Cuánto cuesta una gorra negra?

_____

2. ¿Cuánto cuestan los pantalones?

_____

3. ¿Las camisas cuestan diez dólares?

_____

4. ¿Cuánto cuesta un traje de baño?

_____

5. ¿Los jeans cuestan mucho?

_____

6. ¿La sudadera azul cuesta veinte dólares?

_____

7. ¿Cuánto cuestan las botas aquí?

_____

8. ¿Los abrigos cuestan mucho?

_____

Realidades B

Capítulo 7A

Nombre _____

Hora _____

Fecha _____

WRITING

Actividad 13

You get a discount at the clothing store where you work after school, so you are going to buy presents for your friends and family there. Write complete sentences telling who you will buy gifts for and why you will choose each person's gift. Use the model to help you.

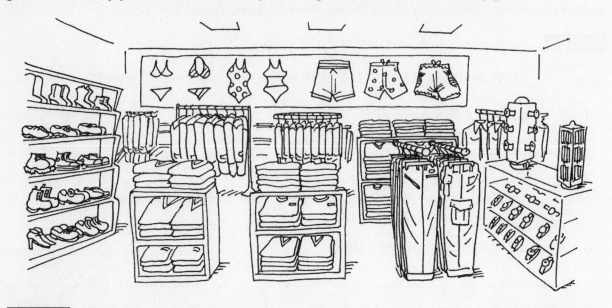

Modelo _Pienso comprar este suéter azul para mi madre porque ella prefiere la ropa del invierno._

1. _____

_____

2. _____

_____

3. _____

_____

4. _____

_____

5. _____

_____

Nombre _____ Hora _____

Fecha _____

VIDEO

Antes de ver el video

Actividad 1

Where do you like to shop? With a partner, write three things you like to buy and the best place to buy them.

Cosas para comprar

_____

_____

_____

Lugares donde comprarlas

_____

_____

_____

¿Comprendes?

Actividad 2

In the video, Claudia and Manolo go many places to find a gift for Manolo's aunt. Look at the places from the video below and number them in the order in which Manolo and Claudia pass them (from beginning to end).

_____ el almacén

_____ la joyería

_____ la tienda de software

_____ la parada de autobuses

_____ el centro comercial

VIDEO

Actividad 3

What happens when Claudia helps Manolo shop? Circle the letter of the correct answers.

1. Manolo necesita comprar un regalo para su tía porque
   a. mañana es su cumpleaños.
   b. mañana es su aniversario de bodas.
   c. mañana es su quinceañera.

2. El año pasado Manolo le compró a su tía
   a. unos aretes en la joyería.
   b. un libro en una librería.
   c. una corbata muy barata.

3. En el centro comercial, ellos ven
   a. videojuegos y software.
   b. pocas cosas en descuento.
   c. anteojos para sol, bolsos, carteras y llaveros.

4. Por fin, deciden comprar para la tía
   a. una cartera.
   b. un collar.
   c. un anillo.

5. Hay una confusión y Manolo le regala a la tía
   a. una pulsera.
   b. unos guantes.
   c. un collar de perro.

Realidades B

Capítulo 7B

Nombre _____

Fecha _____

Hora _____

VIDEO

Y, ¿qué más?

Actividad 4

You are shopping for a birthday gift for your mother. Fill in the dialogue below with your possible responses.

DEPENDIENTE: ¿Qué desea usted?

TÚ: _____

_____

DEPENDIENTE: ¿Prefiere ver ropa, perfumes o joyas para ella?

TÚ: _____

_____

DEPENDIENTE: Aquí hay muchos artículos, pero no cuestan tanto.

TÚ: _____

_____

Realidades B

Capítulo 7B

Nombre _____

Hora _____

Fecha _____

AUDIO

Actividad 5

Sometimes giving gifts is even more fun than receiving them! Listen as people talk about gifts they enjoy giving to their friends and family. Match the pictures below with the corresponding description you hear. Then, in the spaces next to each gift, write where the person bought the gift and what the person paid for it. You will hear each set of statements twice.

	Descripción	Lugar de compra	Precio
1.	_____	_____	_____
2.	_____	_____	_____
3.	_____	_____	_____
4.	_____	_____	_____
5.	_____	_____	_____

Actividad 6

Listen to the following mini-conversations about different kinds of stores. Circle **lógico** if the conversation makes sense and **ilógico** if it does not. You will hear each dialogue twice.

1. lógico   ilógico   **6.** lógico   ilógico

2. lógico   ilógico   **7.** lógico   ilógico

3. lógico   ilógico   **8.** lógico   ilógico

4. lógico   ilógico   **9.** lógico   ilógico

5. lógico   ilógico   **10.** lógico   ilógico

Realidades Ⓑ

Capítulo 7B

Nombre _____

Hora _____

Fecha _____

AUDIO

Actividad 7

Listen as Lorena shows a friend her photographs. Write a sentence describing each one as you hear Lorena describe it. You will hear each conversation twice.

1. Lorena _____ hace _____ .

2. Lorena _____ hace _____ .

3. Lorena _____ hace _____ .

4. Lorena _____ hace _____ .

5. Lorena _____ hace _____ .

Actividad 8

You have been waiting in line all day at the mall, so you have overheard many conversations as you waited. See if you can match each conversation with the illustrations below and write the number of each conversation under the correct illustration. You will hear each conversation twice.

_____ _____ _____ _____

Realidades Ⓑ

Capítulo 7B

Nombre

Fecha

Hora

AUDIO

Actividad 9

As a special holiday service, **El Almacén Continental** is sponsoring a hotline that customers can call to get gift ideas. Listen as callers tell the store specialist what they have bought for a particular person in the past. Then listen to the specialist's suggestion for this year's gift. Use the chart below to take notes. You will hear each conversation twice.

	La personalidad y las actividades de la per-	sona	El regalo del año pasado
1			
2			
3			
4			
5			

Realidades B

Capítulo 7B

Nombre _____

Fecha _____

Hora _____

WRITING

Actividad 10

You are talking to a friend about what you buy when you go shopping. Tell what items you usually buy in each of the specialty shops suggested by the pictures. Then, tell what other items are available at the store. Use the model to help you.

Modelo

En la zapatería, compro zapatos y botas. También es posible comprar guantes y carteras en una zapatería.

1. _____

_____

_____

2. _____

_____

_____

3. _____

_____

_____

Realidades B

Capítulo 7B

Nombre _____

Hora _____

Fecha _____

WRITING

Actividad 11

In your Spanish class, you are asked to learn the dates of some important events in the history and culture of Spanish-speaking countries. To help you memorize these dates, write sentences telling when each event occurred. Follow the model.

Modelo   Pablo Picasso / pintar su cuadro *Guernica* / 1937

Pablo Picasso pintó su cuadro Guernica en 1937.

1. Los Estados Unidos / declarar su independencia / el cuatro de julio, 1776

   _____

2. Vicente Fox / ganar la presidencia de México / 2000

   _____

3. Antonio Banderas / actuar en la película *The Mambo Kings* / 1993

   _____

4. Los jugadores argentinos / ganar la Copa Mundial (*World Cup*) / 1986

   _____

5. Yo / comprar mis primeros zapatos / ???

   _____

6. Nosotros / entrar en la clase de español / ???

   _____

7. Los Juegos Olímpicos / pasar en España / 1992

   _____

8. México / declarar su independencia / el quince de septiembre, 1810

   _____

9. Simón Bolívar / liberar a Venezuela / 1821

   _____

Realidades B

Capítulo 7B

Nombre _____

Hora _____

Fecha _____

WRITING

Actividad 12

The people in your neighborhood were very busy yesterday. Write at least three sentences about what they all did based on the pictures, using at least one of these verbs: **buscar, jugar, pagar, practicar, sacar, tocar.** Follow the model.

Modelo   El Sr. Rodríguez

Ayer el Sr. Rodríguez enseñó la clase de español. La clase practicó la

lección. Los estudiantes usaron las computadoras para hacer las actividades.

1. Andrés

_____

_____

_____

2. yo

_____

_____

_____

3. yo   mi madre

_____

_____

_____

Realidades B

Capítulo 7B

Nombre _____

Hora _____

Fecha _____

WRITING

4. tú

_____

_____

_____

5. Juana e Inés

_____

_____

_____

Actividad 13

You are writing a letter to your aunt in Mexico to tell her what you bought for your family for the holidays. In the letter, tell what you bought for each person, in what stores you found the items, and how much you paid. The letter has been started for you.

Querida Tía:

  Saludos de los Estados Unidos. Te escribo para decirte que terminé de comprar los

regalos para la familia. Para _____ , compré un suéter bonito. ¡Lo encontré en

el almacén por sólo veinte dólares! _____

_____

_____

_____

_____

  Bueno, nos vemos en una semana. ¡Buena suerte con las compras!

Un fuerte abrazo,

Tu sobrino(a) _____

Realidades **B**

Capítulo 8A

Nombre _____ Hora _____

Fecha _____

VIDEO

Antes de ver el video

Actividad 1

You can see and learn a lot on a day trip. Make a list of four places you would like to visit for the day, and write next to each one the main attraction that you would like to see there. Follow the model.

Lugares	Cosas que ver
Modelo *Granada, España*	*La Alhambra*
_____	_____
_____	_____
_____	_____
_____	_____

¿Comprendes?

Actividad 2

Raúl, Gloria, and Tomás went on a day trip to San José and Sarapiquí Park. Under each heading, write the things that they saw in San José and the things that they saw in Sarapiquí Park.

Ministerio de Cultura	mono	Parque España	Catarata La Paz
Gran Terminal del Caribe	palma	bosque lluvioso	Teatro Nacional

San José

_____
_____
_____
_____

Parque Sarapiquí

_____
_____
_____
_____

Realidades B

Capítulo 8A

Nombre _____

Fecha _____

Hora _____

VIDEO

Actividad 3

Based on the video story that you just watched, circle the most appropriate word to complete each statement.

1. Raúl, Gloria y Tomás salieron de la casa muy (tarde / temprano) para ir al parque Sarapiquí.

2. Para ir al parque ellos tomaron el (autobús / avión).

3. El viaje dura (una hora y media / dos horas), porque el parque está a 82 (kilómetros / millas) de San José.

4. En el parque (hace mucho calor / no hace ni frío ni calor) pero llueve mucho.

5. Raúl compra los (libros / boletos) en la Estación Biológica La Selva y cuestan 3,600 (pesos / colones).

6. Tomás tiene la (mochila / cámara) y el (boleto / mapa) y está listo para explorar el parque.

7. Ellos tienen mucho cuidado cuando caminan, pues las raíces de los árboles son muy (grandes / interesantes).

8. Gloria le dice a Tomás: "Hay más de cuatrocientas especies de (monos / aves) en el parque."

9. Ellos tienen problemas al (sacar las fotos / regresar a casa). Pero Tomás (quiere / no quiere) continuar.

10. Raúl dice: "Fue un día (interesante / desastre) pero un poco (difícil / aburrido) para Tomás."

Realidades B

Capítulo 8A

Nombre _____

Hora _____

Fecha _____

VIDEO

Y, ¿qué más?

Actividad 4

Based on what you learned in the video, imagine that you took a field trip to Costa Rica. Your best friend is curious about your trip. Answer your friend's questions below.

1. —¿Cómo es el parque Sarapiquí?

   —_____

2. —¿Sacaste fotos del parque?

   —_____

3. —¿Qué fue lo que más te gustó?

   —_____

4. —¿Qué fue lo que menos te gustó?

   —_____

5. —¿Cuál es la comida típica de Costa Rica?

   —_____

Actividad 5

You call a toll-free telephone number in order to qualify for the popular radio game show, **"Palabras Secretas"** (*Secret Words*). Your challenge is to guess each secret word within ten seconds. Listen to the clues and try to guess the word as the clock is ticking. You must write your answer down before the buzzer in order to be ready for the next one. You will hear each set of statements twice.

1. _____   5. _____
2. _____   6. _____
3. _____   7. _____
4. _____   8. _____

Actividad 6

Listen as a husband and wife talk to a travel agent about their upcoming vacation. Where would each like to go? What type of things would each like to do? Most importantly, do they agree on what is the ideal trip? As you listen, write as much information as you can in each person's travel profile in the chart below. Can you think of a place they could go where both of them would be happy? You will hear this conversation twice.

	EL SEÑOR	LA SEÑORA
¿Adónde le gustaría ir?		
¿Por qué le gustaría ir a ese lugar?		
Cuando va de vacaciones, ¿qué le gustaría hacer?	1. 2.	1. 2.
¿Qué le gustaría ver?	1. 2.	1. 2.
¿Cómo le gustaría viajar?		
¿Adónde deben ir?		

Realidades B

Capítulo 8A

Nombre _____

Fecha _____

Hora _____

AUDIO

Actividad 7

Listen as mothers call their teenaged sons and daughters on their cell phones to see if they have done what they were asked to do. Based on what each teenager says, categorize the answers in the chart. You will hear each conversation twice.

	1	2	3	4	5	6	7	8	9	10
Teen did what the parent asked him or her to do.										
Teen is in the middle of doing what the parent asked him or her to do.										
Teen says he/she is going to do what the parent asked him/her to do.										

Actividad 8

Your Spanish teacher has asked the students in your class to survey each other about a topic of interest. In order to give you a model to follow, your teacher will play a recording of part of a student's survey from last year. Listen to the student's questions, and fill in his survey form. You will hear each conversation twice.

	¿EL LUGAR?
1. Marco	
2. Patricia	
3. Chucho	
4. Rita	
5. Margarita	

Realidades Ⓑ

Capítulo 8A

Nombre _____

Fecha _____

Hora _____

AUDIO

Actividad 9

Everyone loves a superhero, and the listeners of this Hispanic radio station are no exception. Listen to today's episode of "Super Tigre," as the hero helps his friends try to locate the evil Rona Robles! Super Tigre tracks Rona Robles down by asking people when they last saw her and where she went. Keep track of what the people said by filling in the chart. You will hear each conversation twice.

	¿Dónde la vio?	**¿A qué hora la vio?**	**¿Qué hizo ella?** (What did she do?)	**¿Adónde fue ella?**
1				
2				
3				
4				
5				

Where did Super Tigre finally find Rona Robles? _____

Realidades Ⓑ

Capítulo 8A

Nombre _____

Fecha _____

Hora _____

WRITING

Actividad 10

Answer the following questions in complete sentences.

1. ¿Te gusta ir de viaje? ¿Te gustaría más ir de vacaciones al campo o a una ciudad?

_____

_____

2. ¿Visitaste algún parque nacional en el pasado? ¿Cuál(es)? Si no, ¿te gustaría visitar

un parque nacional? _____

_____

3. ¿Vives cerca de un lago? ¿Cómo se llama? ¿Te gusta nadar? ¿Pasear en bote?

_____

_____

4. ¿Te gusta ir al mar? ¿Qué te gusta hacer allí? Si no, ¿por qué no? _____

_____

_____

5. ¿Montaste a caballo alguna vez? ¿Te gustó o no? Si no, ¿te gustaría montar a caballo?

_____

_____

6. Describe tu lugar favorito para vivir. ¿Está cerca de un lago? ¿Cerca o lejos de
la ciudad? ¿Hay montañas / museos / parques / un mar cerca de tu casa ideal?

_____

_____

_____

_____

Nombre _____ Hora _____

Fecha _____ **WRITING**

Actividad 11

You and your friends are talking about what you did over the weekend. Write complete sentences based on the illustrations to tell what the following people did. Follow the model.

Modelo Pablo *vio una película* _____.

1. Mariela y su madre _____.

2. Nosotros _____.

3. Yo _____.

4. Roberto _____.

5. Norma _____.

6. Tú _____.

7. Ignacio e Isabel _____.

Actividad 12

You and your friends were very busy yesterday. Tell all the places where each person went using the illustrations as clues. Follow the model.

Modelo Melisa y su padre _fueron de compras._
Después, fueron al cine.

1. David _____
_____
_____

2. Yo _____
_____
_____

3. Nosotros _____
_____
_____

4. Raquel y Tito _____
_____
_____

Realidades B

Capítulo 8A

Nombre _____

Hora _____

Fecha _____

WRITING

Actividad 13

A. Write two sentences telling what places you visited the last time you went on vacation. You can write about your ideal vacation if you would prefer. Follow the model.

Modelo   *Fui al parque de diversiones.* _____

1. _____

2. _____

B. Write two sentences telling about people you saw when you were on vacation.

Modelo   *Vi a mi abuela.* _____

1. _____

2. _____

C. Now, complete the letter below to your friend. Use your sentences from Part A and Part B and additional details to tell him or her about your vacation.

Querido(a) _____ :

   ¡Hola! ¿Cómo estás? Gracias por tu carta de la semana pasada. Te voy a contar un

poco de nuestras vacaciones del mes pasado. _____

_____

_____

_____

_____

   Y cuando fuimos a otro lugar, vimos _____

_____

_____

_____

_____

_____

                                                    Un abrazo,

                                                    _____

Realidades B

Capítulo 8B

Nombre _____

Hora _____

Fecha _____

VIDEO

Antes de ver el video

Actividad 1

There are lots of things you can do to make the world a better place. Under each category, write two things that you would like to do to help.

Cómo ayudar...

en mi comunidad _____

_____

con el ambiente _____

_____

¿Comprendes?

Actividad 2

In the video, the friends talk about how to help in their communities through volunteer work. Circle the letter of the appropriate answer for each question.

1. Gloria y Raúl trabajan como voluntarios en

    a. un centro de ancianos.

    b. Casa Latina.

    c. el Hospital Nacional de Niños.

2. Tomás va al hospital porque

    a. está enfermo.

    b. a él le encanta el trabajo voluntario.

    c. tiene que llevar ropa para los niños.

3. Gloria dice: "Trabajar con los niños en el hospital es

    a. muy aburrido."

    b. una experiencia inolvidable."

    c. un trabajo que no me gusta."

Realidades **B**

Capítulo 8B

Nombre _____

Hora _____

Fecha _____

VIDEO

4. En su comunidad, Tomás trabaja como voluntario

   a. dando comida a los pobres.

   b. enseñando a leer a los ancianos.

   c. recogiendo ropa usada para los pobres.

5. Ellos también cuidan el ambiente reciclando

   a. aluminio y periódicos.

   b. papel, plástico y vidrio.

   c. papel, vidrio y aluminio.

Actividad 3

Fill in the blanks from the box below to complete the story.

reciclar	importante	libros	pasado
ancianos	comunidad	voluntarios	difícil
lava	simpáticos	trabajo	

En el Hospital Nacional de Niños, Tomás y Gloria trabajan como (1) _____ .

Allí ellos cantan, leen (2) _____ y juegan con los niños. A veces los niños

están muy enfermos y es (3) _____ , pero los niños son muy

(4) _____ . Raúl trabajó en un centro de (5) _____ el año (6)

_____ . Allí les ayudó con la comida y hablando con ellos.

   Tomás también trabaja en su (7) _____ ; él ayuda a recoger ropa usada.

Después la separa, la (8) _____ y luego la da a la gente pobre del barrio.

Es mucho (9) _____ , pero le gusta.

   Todos ellos ayudan a (10) _____ el papel y las botellas pues, piensan que

reciclar y conservar es muy (11) _____ .

Realidades **B**

Capítulo 8B

Nombre

Fecha

Hora

VIDEO

Y, ¿qué más?

Actividad 4

Now that you have seen Tomás, Gloria, and Raúl working in various ways to help others, think about the organizations that make it possible for them to do this work. Imagine that you work with one of the organizations listed below, and write a paragraph about your experiences. Use the model to help you.

el Hospital Nacional de Niños

un centro de ancianos

el club Casa Latina

Modelo   *Me gusta trabajar en el centro de ancianos. Les ayudo con la*
comida y paso tiempo escuchando sus cuentos.

_____

_____

_____

_____

_____

_____

Nombre _____

Hora _____

Fecha _____

AUDIO

Actividad 5

Listen as Sra. Muñoz, the Spanish Club sponsor, asks several students what they did last weekend. If a student's actions had a positive impact on their community, place a check mark in the corresponding box or boxes. If a student's actions had no positive effect on their community, place an *X* in the corresponding box or boxes. You will hear each conversation twice.

	Javier	Ana	José	Celi	Pablo	Laura	Sra. Muñoz
enseñar a los niños a leer							
reciclar la basura de las calles							
jugar al fútbol con amigos							
recoger y lavar la ropa usada para la gente pobre							
trabajar en un centro para ancianos							
traer juguetes a los niños que están en el hospital							
trabajar en un restaurante del centro comercial							

Actividad 6

Listen as people talk about what they did last Saturday. Did they do volunteer work in the community or did they earn spending money for themselves? Place a check mark in the correct box on the grid. You will hear each set of statements twice.

	1	2	3	4	5	6	7	8

Nombre _____ Hora _____

Fecha _____

Actividad 7

Listen as our leaders, friends, and family give advice to teenagers about what we must do to serve our communities. Use the grid below to take notes as you listen. Then, use your notes to complete the sentences below. For example, you might write "El vicepresidente de los Estados Unidos *dice que hay que reciclar la basura de las calles.*" In the last sentence, complete a statement about your personal suggestion for others. You will hear each set of statements twice.

¿Quién(es) lo dice(n)?	¿Qué dice(n)?
1. El presidente de los Estados Unidos	
2. Mis padres	
3. Los médicos del hospital	
4. Mis profesores	
5. Mis amigos y yo	

1. El presidente de los Estados Unidos _____

_____ .

2. Los padres _____

_____ .

3. Los médicos _____

_____ .

4. Los profesores _____

_____ .

5. Mis amigos _____

_____ .

6. Yo _____

_____ .

Realidades Ⓑ

Capítulo 8B

Nombre

Fecha

Hora

AUDIO

Actividad 8

As you hear each of the following statements, imagine whom the speaker might be addressing. Choose from the list of people, and write the number of the statement on the corresponding blank. You will hear each set of statements twice.

_____ al médico   _____ a sus padres

_____ a la policía   _____ a un niño de cinco años

_____ al camarero   _____ a un voluntario del hospital

_____ a la profesora de español   _____ a una persona que trabaja en el zoológico

Actividad 9

Abuela Consuelo always has her grandchildren over for the holidays. She wants to know what they have done over the past year. They also remind her what she gave them last year as a gift. Use the grid to help keep track of each grandchild's story. You will hear each conversation twice.

	¿Qué hizo el niño el año pasado?	¿Qué le dio la abuela al niño el año pasado?
Marta		
Jorge		
Sara		
Miguel		
Angélica		

Actividad 10

Answer the following questions in complete sentences.

1. ¿Hay lugares para hacer trabajo voluntario en tu comunidad?

   _____

   ¿Qué hacen allí? _____

   _____

2. ¿Te gustaría trabajar como voluntario en:

   un hospital? ¿Por qué? _____

   _____

   un centro para personas pobres? ¿Por qué? _____

   _____

   un centro para ancianos? ¿Por qué? _____

   _____

3. ¿Tu familia recicla? _____

   ¿Qué reciclan Uds.? _____

   _____

   ¿Por qué es importante reciclar? _____

   _____

   ¿Te gustaría ayudar con el reciclaje en tu comunidad? _____

   _____

Realidades Ⓑ

Capítulo 8B

Nombre _____

Hora _____

Fecha _____

WRITING

Actividad 11

All of the following people were asked to speak on a subject. You are reporting on what everyone says. Use each item only once. Follow the model.

yo	el trabajo voluntario
nosotros	el campamento de deportes
Sra. Ayala	el reciclaje
Dr. Riviera	el fútbol
tú	el teatro
Paco	la ropa
José y María	la salud
Alicia y yo	los quehaceres

Modelo _La señora Ayala dice que el trabajo voluntario es una_
experiencia inolvidable.

1. _____

2. _____

3. _____

4. _____

5. _____

6. _____

7. _____

Actividad 12

You are finding out what everyone's plans are for the weekend. Choose a verb and a direct object pronoun from the banks and write a sentence about weekend plans for each subject given. Use each verb only once. Follow the model.

ayudar	dar	decir	enseñar	escribir
hacer	invitar	leer	llevar	traer

me	te	le	nos	les

Modelo _Miguel y Elena nos invitan a su fiesta._

1. Mis padres _____.

2. Yo _____.

3. Uds. _____.

4. Nuestra profesora de español _____.

5. El presidente _____.

6. Rafael y Gabriel _____.

7. Tu mejor amigo _____.

8. El Sr. Fuentes _____.

9. La Sra. Allende _____.

10. Tú _____.

Realidades Ⓑ

Capítulo 8B

Nombre _____

Fecha _____

Hora _____

WRITING

Actividad 13

Last week, your Spanish class did some volunteer work at the local nursing home. Read the thank you letter from the residents, then write a paragraph explaining at least four things that you and your classmates did for them. Remember to use the preterite tense and indirect object pronouns where necessary. Follow the model.

Queridos muchachos:

Les escribimos para decirles "gracias" por su generosa visita de la semana pasada. A la señora Blanco le gustó el libro de poesía que Uds. le regalaron. Todos lo pasamos bien. Nos gustó especialmente la canción "Feliz Navidad" que cantó Luisita. El señor Marcos todavía habla de los pasteles que las chicas le trajeron. Y nuestro jardín está más bonito que nunca, después de todo su trabajo. En fin, mil gracias de parte de todos aquí en Pinos Sombreados. Esperamos verles pronto.

Fuertes abrazos,

Los residentes

Modelo *Nosotros visitamos a los residentes de Pinos Sombreados la semana pasada.*

_____

_____

_____

_____

_____

_____

_____

_____

_____

Realidades B

Capítulo 9A

Nombre

Hora

Fecha

VIDEO

Antes de ver el video

Actividad 1

In the second column, write the title of a movie or a television program that is associated with the category in the first column. The first one is done for you.

Programa o película	Nombre del programa o película
telenovelas	"Days of Our Lives"
noticias	
programas de entrevistas	
programas de la vida real	
películas de ciencia ficción	
programas de concurso	
programas educativos	
programas de deportes	
comedias	
dibujos animados	
películas románticas	
programas infantiles	

¿Comprendes?

Actividad 2

Look at the pictures and write what type of program each one is. Then, write the name of the character in the video who likes this type of program.

	CATEGORY	CHARACTER'S NAME
1.	_____	_____
2.	_____	_____
3.	_____	_____
4.	_____	_____
5.	_____	_____

Actividad 3

Using complete sentences, answer the following questions about what happens in the video.

1. ¿Quién tiene el mando a distancia primero?

_____

2. ¿Qué piensa Ana de la telenovela "El amor es loco"?

_____

Realidades **B**

Capítulo 9A

Nombre _____

Fecha _____

Hora _____

VIDEO

3. ¿A quiénes les encantan las telenovelas?

_____

4. ¿Qué piensa Ignacio de los programas de la vida real?

_____

5. ¿Qué piensa Jorgito de escuchar música en el cuarto de su hermana?

_____

6. ¿Qué deciden hacer los amigos al final?

_____

7. ¿Qué quiere ver Elena en el cine? ¿Están de acuerdo Ignacio y Javier?

_____

Y, ¿qué más?

Actividad 4

What kind of TV programs do you like? What type of movies do you enjoy watching? Explain your preferences. Follow the model.

Modelo

A mí me gustan mucho los programas de concursos; son muy divertidos porque puedes jugarlos en casa con tu familia o amigos. Mi hermano prefiere los deportes; siempre quiere el mando a distancia para ver los juegos. Cuando voy al cine prefiero ver comedias, pues las películas románticas son aburridas.

_____

_____

_____

_____

Actividad 5

Your friend is reading you the television line-up for a local television station. After listening to each program description, fill in on the grid what day or days the program is shown, what time it is shown, and what type of program it is. You will hear each set of statements twice.

	Día(s)	Hora	Clase de programa
"Mi computadora"			
"La detective Morales"			
"Cine en su sofá"			
"Las aventuras del Gato Félix"			
"Cara a cara"			
"Lo mejor del béisbol"			
"Marisol"			
"Festival"			
"Treinta minutos"			
"Las Américas"			

Actividad 6

Listen as people in a video rental store talk about what kind of movie they want to rent. After listening to each conversation, put the letter of the type of film they agree on in the space provided. You will hear each conversation twice.

1. _____
2. _____
3. _____
4. _____
5. _____
6. _____
7. _____

A. una película policíaca

B. una comedia

C. un drama

D. una película de ciencia ficción

E. una película romántica

F. una película de horror

G. una película de dibujos animados

Realidades **B**

Capítulo 9A

Nombre _____

Hora _____

Fecha _____

AUDIO

Actividad 7

Listen to a film critic interviewing five people on opening night of the movie *Marruecos*. After listening to each person's interview, circle the number of stars that closely matches the person's opinion of the movie, from a low rating of one star to a high rating of four. After noting all of the opinions, give the movie an overall rating of one to four stars, and give a reason for your answer. You will hear each conversation twice.

	No le gustó nada	Le gustó más o menos	Le gustó mucho	Le encantó
1.	[★]	[★★]	[★★★]	[★★★★]
2.	[★]	[★★]	[★★★]	[★★★★]
3.	[★]	[★★]	[★★★]	[★★★★]
4.	[★]	[★★]	[★★★]	[★★★★]
5.	[★]	[★★]	[★★★]	[★★★★]

¿Cuántas estrellas para *Marruecos*? ¿Por qué? _____

_____

Actividad 8

Listen as two friends talk on the phone about what they just saw on TV. Do they seem to like the same type of programs? As you listen to their conversation, fill in the Venn diagram, indicating: 1) which programs only Alicia likes; 2) which programs both Alicia and Laura like; and 3) which programs only Laura likes. You will hear this conversation twice.

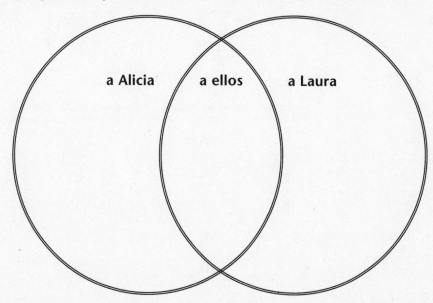

a Alicia   a ellos   a Laura

Nombre _____

Hora _____

Fecha _____

AUDIO

Actividad 9

Listen as a television critic reviews some of the new shows of the season. As you listen, determine which shows he likes and dislikes, and why. Fill in the chart. You will hear each paragraph twice.

	Le gusta...	¿Por qué le gusta?	No le gusta...	¿Por qué no le gusta?
1				
2				
3				
4				
5				

Realidades B

Capítulo 9A

Nombre _____

Hora _____

Fecha _____

WRITING

Actividad 10

Answer the following questions about movies and television.

1. ¿Te gusta ir al cine?

_____

2. ¿Prefieres los dramas o las comedias? ¿Por qué? _____

_____

_____

3. ¿Cómo se llama tu película favorita? ¿Qué clase de película es?

_____

_____

4. ¿Te gustan las películas policíacas? ¿Por qué? _____

_____

5. ¿Te gusta más ver le tele o leer? ¿Por qué? _____

_____

_____

6. ¿Qué clase de programas prefieres? ¿Por qué? _____

_____

_____

7. ¿Cuántos canales de televisión puedes ver en casa? _____

¿Cuál es tu canal favorito? _____

¿Por qué? _____

8. ¿Tienes un programa favorito? ¿Cómo se llama? _____

_____

Realidades Ⓑ

Capítulo 9A

Nombre _____

Hora _____

Fecha _____

WRITING

Actividad 11

Your school newspaper printed a picture of the preparations for the Cinco de Mayo party at your school. Describe the photo using a form of **acabar de** + infinitive to tell what everyone just finished doing before the picture was taken.

Modelo *Horacio Ibáñez acaba de sacar la foto.* _____

1. Isabel _____

_____

2. Julia y Ramón _____

_____

3. Yo _____

_____

4. La señora Lemaños _____

_____

5. Ana _____

_____

WRITING

Actividad 12

You and your friends are talking about movies. Tell about people's preferences by choosing a subject from the first column and matching it with words from the other two columns to make complete sentences. Use each subject only once, but words from the other columns can be used more than once. Follow the model.

nosotros	gustar	las películas románticas
mis padres	encantar	las película de horror
mí	aburrir	las películas policíacas
ti	interesar	las comedias
los profesores	disgustar	los dramas
mis amigas		
mi abuelo		

Modelo *A mí me encantan las películas románticas.*

1. _____

2. _____

3. _____

4. _____

5. _____

6. _____

Realidades Ⓑ

Capítulo 9A

Nombre _____

Hora _____

Fecha _____

WRITING

Actividad 13

You are writing your new Spanish-speaking pen pal an e-mail about American television. First tell him about a program that you just saw. What type of show was it? Did you like it? Was it interesting? Then, tell him about two other types of TV shows that are popular in America. Make sure to tell him your opinion of these types of shows, and what some other people you know think about them.

Fecha: 20 de abril

Tema: La televisión

Querido Pancho:

   ¡Hola! ¿Cómo estás? Acabo de terminar de ver el programa _____

_____ . A mí _____

_____

_____

_____

   En los Estados Unidos, la gente ve mucho la tele. _____

_____

_____

_____

_____

¡Te escribo pronto!

                     Un abrazo,

                    _____

Realidades (B)

Capítulo 9B

Nombre _____

Fecha _____

Hora _____

VIDEO

Antes de ver el video

Actividad 1

How do you communicate with your friends from far away? Using the word bank below, write two sentences about how you might stay in touch with long distance friends.

cámara digital	correo electrónico
ordenador / computadora	cibercafé
navegar en la Red	página Web
información	salones de chat
dirección electrónica	foto digital

_____

_____

_____

_____

¿Comprendes?

Actividad 2

Javier is becoming accustomed to living in Spain, but he has a lot to learn about technology. What does Ana teach him? Write **cierto** (*true*) or **falso** (*false*) next to each statement.

1. Javier conoce muy bien las cámaras digitales. _____

2. Él va a enviar una tarjeta a su amigo Esteban. _____

3. Javier le saca una foto de Ana y le gusta la cámara. _____

4. Él piensa que no es muy complicada la cámara digital. _____

5. Ana lo lleva a un cibercafé, para ordenar un café. _____

6. Empiezan a navegar en la Red. _____

7. Ana busca su página Web, pero Javier no la quiere ver. _____

8. No hay mucha información en la Red. _____

9. Pueden visitar los salones de chat, pero
prefieren escribirle un correo electrónico a Esteban. _____

10. Esteban ve la foto digital de su amigo y piensa que está triste. _____

Actividad 3

Complete the sentences below with information from the video.

1. Javier va a enviar _____ a
su amigo Esteban.

2. Ana saca muchas fotos con su
_____ .

3. A Javier le gusta la cámara de Ana porque no
es muy _____ .

4. Ana y Javier van a un _____ para
escribirle a Esteban por _____ electrónico.

5. Según Ana, el ordenador _____
para mucho.

6. Javier quiere saber qué tal fue el _____
de Cristina.

Realidades B

Capítulo 9B

Nombre _____

Hora _____

Fecha _____

VIDEO

Y, ¿qué más?

Actividad 4

You heard Ana and Javier talk about the many ways they use computers. Write a paragraph describing your two favorite ways to use a computer. Use the model to give you an idea of how to start.

Modelo   *En mi casa todos usan la computadora. Para mí el uso más importante es...*

_____

_____

_____

_____

_____

_____

_____

Nombre _____ Hora _____

Fecha _____

AUDIO

Actividad 5

While navigating a new Web site, two friends click on a link to a self-quiz to find out if they are **CiberAdictos.** Based on their discussion of each question, write in the chart below whether you think they answered **sí** or **no.** According to the Web site, a score of more than six **sí** answers determines that you are a **CiberAdicto.** You will hear each set of statements twice.

	1	2	3	4	5	6	7	8	¿Es CiberAdicto?
Rafael									
Miguel									

Actividad 6

Víctor has studied for the first quiz in his beginning technology class. As the teacher reads each statement, he is to answer **falso** or **cierto.** Listen to the statements and write the answers in the boxes, and take the quiz too. Would you be able to score 100%? You will hear each statement twice.

1	2	3	4	5	6	7	8	9	10

Actividad 7

Listen to the following conversations that you overhear while sitting at a table in the Café Mariposa. After listening to what each person is saying, write what they asked for in the first column and what they were served in the second column. You will hear each statement twice.

Persona	Comida pedida	Comida servida
1. Señor Cruz		
2. Señora Vargas		
3. Señor Ávila		
4. Marcelo y Daniele		
5. Señor Urbina		
6. Señora Campos		
7. Señora Suerte		

Actividad 8

Listen as teenagers talk to each other about what they need to learn how to do. The second teenager is always able to suggest someone whom the first teenager should ask for help. Match the person who is suggested to the correct picture. You will hear each set of statements twice.

Actividad 9

Listen as two people discuss how the computer and the Internet have changed our lives. As you listen, organize their points into two columns by summarizing what they say. You will hear each set of statements twice.

Antes de la computadora y la Red	Después de la computadora y la Red
1. _____	_____
2. _____	_____
3. _____	_____
4. _____	_____

Realidades B

Capítulo 9B

Nombre _____

Fecha _____

Hora _____

WRITING

Actividad 10

Read the following ad about a computer of the future. Then, answer the questions below.

CEREBRADOR: ¡EL FUTURO AHORA!

¿Está cansado de ver las computadoras del futuro en una película o de leer sobre ellas en una novela? ¿Quiere el futuro ahora? ¡Pues **Cerebrador** lo tiene!

♦ La información, los gráficos, la música en la Red...
   ¡todo sin límite!

♦ Grabar un disco, escribir un informe, navegar en la Red...
   ¡sólo hay que pensarlo y se logra en poco tiempo!

♦ ¿Tiene problemas de conexión o detesta sentarse a usar la computadora?
   Sólo necesita **Cerebrador** *y dos metros de espacio para poder ver todo en la pantalla: documentos, correo electrónico, su página Web, etc. Conecte a su propia cabeza.*

Con **Cerebrador** puede sacar fotos con una minicámara digital y crear diapositivas con ellas.

Llame ahora para pedir este fenómeno.

---

1. ¿Cómo se llama la computadora del anuncio?

_____

2. ¿Qué dice el anuncio que Ud. puede hacer con esta computadora?

_____

_____

_____

3. ¿Qué necesita para usar una computadora? ¿Es una computadora portátil?

_____

_____

_____

4. ¿Cree Ud. que es posible comprar una computadora como ésta? ¿Por qué?

_____

_____

_____

_____

Actividad 11

Your favorite restaurant has great food, but the wait staff is always messing up the orders. Using the pictures as clues and the correct forms of the verbs **pedir** and **servir**, write what happens when the following people order their meals. Follow the model and remember to use the proper indirect object pronouns in your sentences.

Modelo   Yo   El camarero

Yo pido pescado pero el camarero me sirve pollo.

1.

    Tú   Ellos

    _____

2.

    Nosotros   La camarera

    _____

3.

    María   Uds.

    _____

4.

    Ellos   Nosotros

    _____

5.

    Ramón y Yo   Los camareros

    _____

WRITING

Actividad 12

Answer the following questions in 2–3 complete sentences using the verbs **saber** and/or **conocer**.

1. ¿Eres talentoso(a)? ¿Qué sabes hacer? ¿Tienes unos amigos muy talentosos? ¿Qué saben hacer ellos?

    _____

    _____

    _____

    _____

2. ¿Conoces a alguna persona famosa? ¿Quién? ¿Cómo es? ¿Alguien más en tu familia conoce a una persona famosa?

    _____

    _____

    _____

    _____

3. ¿Qué ciudades o países conocen tú y tu familia? ¿Cuándo los visitaste? ¿Qué lugares conocen tus amigos?

    _____

    _____

    _____

    _____

4. ¿Qué sabes de la geografía de Latinoamérica? (¿Sabes cuál es la capital de Uruguay? ¿Sabes cuántos países hay en Sudamérica?)

    _____

    _____

    _____

    _____

Realidades **B**

Capítulo 9B

Nombre _____

Hora _____

Fecha _____

WRITING

Actividad 13

Describe the **cibercafé** below. First, tell three things that you can do there. Next, tell three items that they serve at the café, using the verb **servir** and the food items in the picture. Finally, tell what you can do if you need assistance at the **cibercafé.** Use the verb **pedir**, and the verbs **saber** and **conocer** to discuss how knowledgeable the staff is (**Ellos saben ayudar.../ Ellos conocen bien la Red...**).

Ud. puede _____

_____

_____

_____

Allí ellos _____

_____

_____

_____

_____

_____

_____

_____

_____

Song Lyrics

These are the lyrics for the songs that appear on the Canciones CD.

Track 01

ALEGRE VENGO

Alegre vengo de la montaña
De mi cabaña que alegre está
A mis amigos les traigo flores
De las mejores de mi rosal
A mis amigos les traigo flores
De las mejores de mi rosal

Ábreme la puerta
Ábreme la puerta
Que estoy en la calle
Y dirá la gente
Que esto es un desaire
Y dirá la gente
Que esto es un desaire

A la sarandela, a la sarandela
A la sarandela, de mi corazón
A la sarandela, a la sarandela
A la sarandela, de mi corazón

Allá dentro veo, allá dentro veo
Un bulto tapado
No sé si será un lechón asado
No sé si será un lechón asado
A la sarandela...

Track 02

LA MARIPOSA

Vamos todos a cantar,
vamos todos a bailar
la morenada.

Vamos todos a cantar,
vamos todos a bailar
la morenada.

Con los tacos,
con las manos.
¡Viva la fiesta!

Con los tacos,
con las manos.
¡Viva la fiesta!

Track 03

ERES TÚ

Como una promesa eres tú, eres tú
como una mañana de verano;
como una sonrisa eres tú, eres tú;
así, así eres tú.

Toda mi esperanza eres tú, eres tú,
como lluvia fresca en mis manos;
como fuerte brisa eres tú, eres tú
así, así eres tú.

[estribillo]
Eres tú como el agua de mi fuente;
eres tú el fuego de mi hogar.
Eres tú como el fuego de mi hoguera;
eres tú el trigo de mi pan.

Como mi poema eres tú, eres tú;
como una guitarra en la noche.
Todo mi horizonte eres tú, eres tú;
así, así eres tú.

Eres tú como el agua de mi fuente;
eres tú el fuego de mi hogar.
Algo así eres tú;
algo así como el fuego de mi hoguera.
Algo así eres tú;
Mi vida, algo, algo así eres tú.

Eres tú como el fuego de mi hoguera;
eres tú el trigo de mi pan.
Algo así eres tú;
algo así como el fuego de mi hoguera.
Algo así eres tú;

Track 04

LA CUCARACHA

[estribillo]
La cucaracha, la cucaracha,
ya no quiere caminar,
porque no tiene, porque le falta
dinero para gastar.

La cucaracha, la cucaracha,
ya no quiere caminar,
porque no tiene, porque le falta
dinero para gastar.

Una cucaracha pinta
le dijo a una colorada:
Vámonos para mi tierra
a pasar la temporada.

Una cucaracha pinta
le dijo a una colorada:
Vámonos para mi tierra
a pasar la temporada.

La cucaracha, la cucaracha,
ya no quiere caminar,
porque no tiene, porque le falta
dinero para gastar.

Todas las muchachas tienen
en los ojos dos estrellas,
pero las mexicanitas
de seguro son más bellas.

Todas las muchachas tienen
en los ojos dos estrellas,
pero las mexicanitas
de seguro son más bellas.

La cucaracha, la cucaracha,
ya no quiere caminar,
porque no tiene, porque le falta
dinero para gastar.

Una cosa me da risa,
Pancho Villa sin camisa,
ya se van los carrancistas,
porque vienen los villistas.

Una cosa me da risa,
Pancho Villa sin camisa,
ya se van los carrancistas,
porque vienen los villistas.

La cucaracha, la cucaracha,
ya no quiere caminar,
porque no tiene, porque le falta
dinero para gastar.

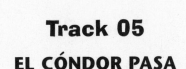

Track 05

EL CÓNDOR PASA

Al cóndor de los Andes despertó
una luz,
una luz,
de un bello amanecer, amanecer.

Sus alas en lo alto extendió
y bajó,
y bajó,
al dulce manantial, para beber.

La nieve de las cumbres brilla ya
bajo el sol, el día y la luz.
La nieve de las cumbres brilla ya
bajo el sol, el día y la luz,
del bello amanecer, amanecer.

Al cóndor de los Andes despertó
una luz,
una luz,
de un bello amanecer, amanecer.

Sus alas en lo alto extendió
y bajó,
y bajó,
al dulce manantial, para beber.

La nieve de las cumbres brilla ya
bajo el sol, el día y la luz.
La nieve de las cumbres brilla ya
bajo el sol, el día y la luz,
del bello amanecer, amanecer.

Track 06

ASÓMATE AL BALCÓN

Asómate al balcón para que veas mi
parranda
Asómate al balcón para que veas
quien te canta
Asómate al balcón para que veas tus
amigos
Asómate al balcón
Formemos un vacilón

Asómate, asómate, asómate, asómate

Yo sé que quieres dormir
Pero así es la Navidad
Y si tú no te levantas
Te sacamos de la cama
Aunque tengas que pelear

Asómate al balcón para (se repite)

¡Asómate, asómate, asómate, asómate!

Track 07

LA BAMBA

Para bailar la bamba, para bailar la bamba
se necesita una poca de gracia,
una poca de gracia y otra cosita
y arriba y arriba,
y arriba y arriba y arriba iré,
yo no soy marinero, yo no soy marinero,
por ti seré, por ti seré, por ti seré.

Bamba, bamba...

Una vez que te dije, una vez que te dije
que eras bonita, se te puso la cara,
se te puso la cara coloradita
y arriba y arriba,
y arriba y arriba y arriba iré,
yo no soy marinero, yo no soy marinero,
soy capitán, soy capitán, soy capitán.

Bamba, bamba...

Para subir al cielo, para subir al cielo
se necesita una escalera grande,
una escalera grande y otra chiquita
y arriba y arriba,
y arriba y arriba y arriba iré,
yo no soy marinero, yo no soy marinero,
por ti seré, por ti seré, por ti seré.

Bamba, bamba...

Track 08

HIMNO DEL ATHLETIC DE BILBAO

Tiene Bilbao un gran tesoro
que adora y mima con gran pasión.
Su club de fútbol
de bella historia,
lleno de gloria,
mil veces campeón.

Athletic, Athletic club
de limpia tradición,
ninguno más que tú
lleva mejor blasón.

Del fútbol eres rey,
te llaman el león
y la afición el rey
del fútbol español.

Cantemos pues los bilbainitos,
a nuestro club con gran amor,
para animarle con nuestro himno,
el canto digno del Alirón.

¡Alirón! ¡Alirón!
el Athletic es campeón.

Track 9

PARA ROMPER LA PIÑATA

Echen confites y canelones
pa' los muchachos
que son comilones.
Castaña asada, piña cubierta,
pa' los muchachos que van a la puerta.

Ándale, Lola,
no te dilates

con la canasta
de los cacahuates.

En esta posada
nos hemos chasqueado,
porque la dueña
nada nos ha dado.

Track 10

PIÑATA

Dale, dale, dale,
no pierdas el tino,

mide la distancia
que hay en el camino.

Track 11

LAS MAÑANITAS

Éstas son las mañanitas
que cantaba el Rey David,
pero no eran tan bonitas
como las cantan aquí.

[estribillo]
Despierta, mi bien, despierta,
mira que ya amaneció,
ya los pajarillos cantan,
la luna ya se metió.

Despierta, mi bien, despierta,
mira que ya amaneció,
ya los pajarillos cantan,
la luna ya se metió.

Si el sereno de la esquina
me quisiera hacer favor,
de apagar su linternita
mientras que pasa mi amor.

[estribillo]
Despierta, mi bien, despierta,
mira que ya amaneció,
ya los pajarillos cantan,
la luna ya se metió.

Despierta, mi bien, despierta,
mira que ya amaneció,
ya los pajarillos cantan,
la luna ya se metió.

Track 12

DE COLORES

De colores, de colores se visten los
campos en la primavera.
De colores, de colores son los pajaritos
que vienen de afuera.
De colores, de colores es el arco iris
que vemos salir.
Y por eso los grandes amores de
muchos colores me gustan a mí.
Y por eso los grandes amores de
muchos colores me gustan a mí.

De colores, de colores brillantes y finos
se viste la aurora.
De colores, de colores son los mil
reflejos que el sol atesora.
De colores, de colores se viste el
diamante que vemos lucir.
Y por eso los grandes amores de
muchos colores me gustan a mí.
Y por eso los grandes amores de
muchos colores me gustan a mí.

Track 13

QUIÉREME MUCHO

Quiéreme mucho, dulce amor mío,
que amante siempre te adoraré.
Yo con tus besos y tus caricias
mis sufrimientos acallaré.

Cuando se quiere de veras,
como te quiero yo a ti,
es imposible, mi cielo,
tan separados vivir.

Cuando se quiere de veras,
como te quiero yo a ti,
es imposible, mi cielo,
tan separados vivir,
tan separados vivir.

Es imposible, mi cielo,
tan separados vivir,
tan separados vivir, vivir.

MÉXICO LINDO Y QUERIDO

Voz de la guitarra mía,
al despertar la mañana,
quiere cantar su alegría
a mi tierra mexicana.

Yo le canto a tus volcanes,
a tus praderas y flores
que son como talismanes
del amor de mis amores.

México lindo y querido
si muero lejos de ti
que digan que estoy dormido
y que me traigan aquí.

México lindo y querido
si muero lejos de ti
que digan que estoy dormido
y que me traigan aquí.

Voz de la guitarra mía,
al despertar la mañana,
quiere cantar su alegría
a mi tierra mexicana.

Yo le canto a tus volcanes,
a tus praderas y flores
que son como talismanes
del amor de mis amores.

México lindo y querido
si muero lejos de ti
que digan que estoy dormido
y que me traigan aquí.

México lindo y querido
si muero lejos de ti
que digan que estoy dormido
y que me traigan aquí.

Track 15

MI CAFETAL

Porque la gente vive criticándome
Me paso la vida sin pensar en ná

Porque la gente vive criticándome
Paso la vida sin pensar en ná

Pero no sabiendo que yo soy el hombre
Que tengo un hermoso y lindo cafetal

Pero no sabiendo que yo soy el hombre
Que tengo un hermoso y lindo cafetal

Yo tengo mi cafetal
Y tú ya no tienes ná...

Yo tengo mi cafetal
Y tú ya no tienes ná...

Colombia mi tierra bonita

Nada me importa que la gente diga
Que no tengo plata que no tengo ná

Nada me importa que la gente diga
Que no tengo plata que no tengo ná

Pero no sabiendo que yo soy el hombre
Que tengo un hermoso y lindo cafetal

Pero no sabiendo que yo soy el hombre
Que tengo un hermoso y lindo cafetal

Yo tengo mi cafetal
Y tú ya no tienes ná..

Yo tengo mi cafetal
Y tú ya no tienes ná..

Track 16

MARÍA ISABEL

La playa estaba desierta,
el mar bañaba tu piel,
cantando con mi guitarra
para ti, María Isabel.

La playa estaba desierta,
el mar bañaba tu piel,
cantando con mi guitarra
para ti, María Isabel.

[estribillo]
Toma tu sombrero y póntelo,
vamos a la playa, calienta el sol.

Toma tu sombrero y póntelo,
vamos a la playa, calienta el sol.

Chiri biri bi, poro, pom, pom.
Chiri biri bi, poro, pom, pom.
Chiri biri bi, poro, pom, pom.
Chiri biri bi, poro, pom, pom.

En la arena escribí tu nombre
y luego yo lo borré
para que nadie pisara
tu nombre: María Isabel.

En la arena escribí tu nombre
y luego yo lo borré
para que nadie pisara
tu nombre: María Isabel.

[estribillo]
Toma tu sombrero y póntelo,
vamos a la playa, calienta el sol.

Toma tu sombrero y póntelo,
vamos a la playa, calienta el sol.

Chiri biri bi, poro, pom, pom.
Chiri biri bi, poro, pom, pom.
Chiri biri bi, poro, pom, pom.
Chiri biri bi, poro, pom, pom.

La luna fue caminando,
bajo las olas del mar;
tenía celos de tus ojos
y tu forma de mirar.

La luna fue caminando,
bajo las olas del mar;
tenía celos de tus ojos
y tu forma de mirar.

[estribillo]
Toma tu sombrero y póntelo,
vamos a la playa, calienta el sol.

Toma tu sombrero y póntelo,
vamos a la playa, calienta el sol.

Chiri biri bi, poro, pom, pom.
Chiri biri bi, poro, pom, pom.
Chiri biri bi, poro, pom, pom.
Chiri biri bi, poro, pom, pom.

Track 17

LA GOLONDRINA

A donde irá veloz y fatigada,
la golondrina que de aquí se irá,
allí en el cielo se mirará angustiada,
sin paz ni abrigo que dio mi amor.

Junto a mi pecho allí hará su nido,
En donde pueda la estacion pasar,
También yo estoy en la región perdida.
¡Oh cielo santo! Y sin poder volar.

También yo estoy en la región perdida.
¡Oh cielo santo! Y sin poder volar.

Junto a mi pecho allí hará su nido,
En donde pueda la estacion pasar,
También yo estoy en la región perdida.
¡Oh cielo santo! Y sin poder volar.

Track 18

¡VIVA JUJUY!

Vamos con ese bailecito

Adentrito cholo

¡Viva Jujuy!
¡Viva la Puna!
¡Viva mi amada!
¡Vivan los cerros
pintarrajeados
de mi quebrada...!

¡Viva Jujuy!
¡Viva la Puna!
¡Viva mi amada!
¡Vivan los cerros
pintarrajeados
de mi quebrada...!

De mi quebrada
humahuaqueña...

No te separes
de mis amores,
¡tú eres mi dueña!

La, lara, rara, rara

No te separes
de mis amores,
¡tú eres mi dueña!

Dos, dos y se va la otrita

Adentro

Viva Jujuy
y la hermosura
de las jujeñas!
Vivan las trenzas
bien renegridas
de mi morena!

Viva Jujuy
y la hermosura
de las jujeñas!
Vivan las trenzas
bien renegridas
de mi morena!

De mi morena
mal pagadora

No te separes
de mis amores
¡tú eres mi dueña!

La, lara, rara, rara

No te separes
de mis amores
¡tú eres mi dueña!

Track 19

ADIÓS MUCHACHOS

Adiós muchachos compañeros de mi vida,
barra querida, de aquellos tiempos.
Me toca a mí hoy emprender la retirada,
debo alejarme de mi buena muchachada.

Adiós, muchachos,
ya me voy y me resigno,
contra el destino nadie la talla.
Se terminaron para mí todas las farras.
Mi cuerpo enfermo no resiste más.

Dos lágrimas sinceras
derramo en mi partida
por la barra querida
que nunca me olvidó.
Y al darle a mis amigos
mi adiós postrero
les doy con toda el alma
mi bendición.

Adiós muchachos compañeros de mi vida,
barra querida, de aquellos tiempos.
Me toca a mí hoy emprender la retirada,
debo alejarme de mi buena muchachada.

Adiós, muchachos,
ya me voy y me resigno,
contra el destino nadie la talla.
Se terminaron para mí todas las farras.
Mi cuerpo enfermo no resiste más.

FCAT Support
and Test Practice

FCAT Support Level B

Art, Photo, and Map Credits

Page 11: © John Neubauer/PhotoEdit; **Page 12:** (t) © Sisse Brimberg/NGS Image Collection, (b) © Dave Albers/Illustration Works, Inc.; **Page 17:** Ted Smykal; **Page 22:** (t) © Michelle Chaplow/CORBIS, (b) © Patrick Ward/CORBIS; **Page 27:** (map) Ted Smykal, Geoffrey Clifford/ASA/IPN Stock; **Page 32:** (t) The Textile Museum, Washington, D.C., no. 91.192 detail, (b) The Textile Museum, Washington D.C., no. 91.99; **Page 37:** © Michael Krasowitz/FPG; **Page 42:** (map) Ted Smykal, Jack Parsons/Omni-Photo Communications, Inc.; **Page 43:** Glenn LeBlanc/Index Stock Imagery, Inc.; **Page 48:** (t) © Nik Wheeler/CORBIS, (b) © Robert Frerck/Odyssey/Chicago; **Page 53:** (t) © AFP/CORBIS, (b) © Univision Network 2000; **Page 58:** (both) Reuters Newmedia, Inc., Inc./CORBIS.

To the Student

Did you know that becoming a better reader in Spanish can improve your scores on standardized reading tests in English and Spanish? Research has shown that the skills you develop by reading in a second language are transferred to reading in your first language. Research also shows that the more you practice for standardized tests and work on test-taking strategies, the more your scores will improve. The goals of this section of the *REALIDADES* Practice Workbook with Writing, Audio & Video Activities with FCAT Support are (1) to provide readings in both Spanish and English, (2) extra practice with test-taking strategies, and (3) to help you improve your FCAT reading skills.

Getting to Know the Test

The test practice in this book offers a variety of readings to reflect the types of passages you might expect to find on the FCAT reading test. It also provides practice for two different types of questions you are apt to encounter on such a test: multiple choice and Short Response.

Multiple Choice

Multiple choice questions always have four answer choices. Pick the <u>one</u> that is the best answer. A correct answer is worth one point and should take one minute per item to answer.

Short Response

This symbol appears next to questions requiring short written answers:

The Short Response task requires you to write a short response to a question or statement. Short Response tasks are worth two points. Each task should take approximately five minutes to complete. Your responses are scored zero, one, or two points depending on the accuracy of the response.

Note: Although the *REALIDADES* readings are written in Spanish, you may answer the questions in English. Since you will have to read several selections in Spanish, you will also have to make sure that you completely understand the passages in order to answer the questions.

Working With The Test Practice

Your teacher will assign the test practice for classwork or homework, or you might be doing the test practice on your own. Each reading is followed by questions, and the answer sheet immediately follows the questions. For multiple choice questions, you should bubble-in the response. For Short Response questions, write your answers on the lines provided.

Tips for Improving Your Score

Before Taking the Tests

Do something relaxing the night before. Then get a good night's sleep, and be sure to eat a nutritious meal before the test. Wear comfortable clothing.

Know What You Are Being Asked

Read all questions carefully, and ask yourself, "What are they asking me?" The purpose of the *REALIDADES* FCAT Support section as well as the FCAT reading tests, is to measure students' achievement in constructing meaning from a wide variety of texts. Reading passages may be either literary, including fiction, nonfiction, poetry or drama; or informational type texts including different points of view, issues, conflicts, or problems.

Here is a list of basic reading skills that you should know:
- Understanding major ideas, details, and organization
- Drawing conclusions
- Understanding cause and effect
- Comparing and contrasting
- Finding, interpreting, and organizing information
- Understanding author's purpose and/or viewpoint
- Understanding character and plot development

Always read the questions <u>before</u> you read the passage. This will help you focus on the task. Watch your time!

Allot a specific amount of time per question—approximately one minute for multiple choice, and three to five minutes for Short Response questions. Do not spend too much time on any one question, and monitor your time so that you will be able to complete the test.

Show what you know, relax, and think positively. Above all, relax. It's natural to be nervous, but think positively. Just do your best!

Multiple Choice Questions: Helpful Hints

Multiple choice questions have only one right answer. There is no "creative" response, only a correct one. This section of the *REALIDADES* Practice Workbook with Writing, Audio & Video Activities with FCAT Support provides extensive practice for the types of Multiple choice items that you might find on the FCAT. There are four answer choices (A, B, C, D or F, G, H, I) per question. Allot approximately one minute to answer a Multiple choice question. Answers are worth one point each. Read the question carefully. Multiple choice answers are either right or wrong. Eliminate obvious wrong answers by lightly crossing them out. You will receive credit and one point if you select the correct answer.

Short Response Questions: Helpful Hints

- Read the question <u>before</u> reading the passage.
- Re-read the question as you prepare to respond: Are you being asked to list, describe, explain, discuss, persuade, or compare and contrast?
- Look back at the passage as often as necessary to answer the question correctly. Underline any key sections that you think might be important to your response.
- Use the margins next to the passage to jot down thoughts and ideas and to prepare a brief outline of what you will include in your answer. Your first sentence should be clear and provide your main point. Each sentence after the first should include supporting details and information from the reading to support your answer. Always remember to include <u>evidence</u> from the reading to support your answer! You will find these supporting details and information in the readings, charts, maps, graphs, and illustrations. Try to include two or three details that you have paraphrased or put into your own words.
- Proofread your response to make sure you have expressed your thoughts well. Use good grammar and make sure your handwriting is legible. Write your answer only in the box provided. Anything that you write outside the box or in the margins will not be graded on the FCAT.

How the Test Will Be Scored

It is important to know in advance how responses will be scored. This will lower your anxiety level and help you focus. For the purpose of these practice tests, you can assume the following:

Multiple Choice Questions

Multiple choice answers are either right or wrong. You will receive credit and one point if you select the correct answer. You should:

- Try to identify the answer before you examine the choices.
- Eliminate obviously incorrect choices by lightly crossing them out.
- Try to narrow the choices down to two.

Performance-Based Questions (Short Response)

Short Response questions are called "performance tasks." They are often scored with rubrics, which describe a range of performance. You will receive credit for how close your answers come to the correct response. The performance tasks on these practice tests will require thoughtful answers. You must:

- <u>Read</u> the passage.
- <u>Think</u> about the question as it relates to the passage, and
- <u>Explain</u> your answer by citing general ideas and supporting details from the passage.
  or:
- <u>Create</u> a written document (a letter, for example) that clearly uses or models information provided in the reading passage.

Rubric for Short Response Questions

2 points The response indicates that the student has a complete understanding of the reading concept embodied in the task. The student has provided a response that is accurate, complete, and fulfills all the requirements of the task. Necessary support and/or examples are included, and the information given is clearly text-based. Any extensions beyond the text are relevant to the task.

1 point The response indicates that the student has a partial understanding of the reading concept embodied in the task. The student has provided a response that may include information that is essentially correct and text-based, but the information is too general or too simplistic. Some of the support and/or examples may be incomplete or omitted.

0 points The response is inaccurate, confused, and/or irrelevant, or the student has failed to respond to the task.

Secret Strategies

Here are some secret strategies for success on reading tests such as the ones you will find in this workbook as well as on the FCAT itself! *¡Lee las estratégias con cuidado!*

How You Can Find the Main Idea

The main idea is the most important subject or message the author is trying to say. Look at the title, heading, subheading; first and last sentences of the paragraphs; repeated words/phrases; bold type words, names, or phrases in the passage. Every time you read a paragraph, write three or four word margin notes, which identify the main idea for each paragraph. You will see that the author supports the main idea with details in the passages. Sometimes when a question is asking for a main idea, it might ask for another title for this passage, another subheading for a paragraph or what the author is trying to say, or the moral or message of the story. The main idea and its supporting details are organized in patterns. If you can distinguish the reading's organizational patterns, then you can figure out the main idea.

Can You Recognize an Organizational Pattern?

How You Can Recognize Time Order

Time order is a pattern where the details or events are arranged in an order in which they happen. Sometimes the events happen in chronological order. You will see words like "first" *(primero)*, "in the beginning" *(al principio)*, "before" *(antes, antes de)*, "as soon as" *(tan pronto como)*, "during" *(durante)*, "second" *(segundo)*, "meanwhile" *(mientras tanto)*, "after" *(después)*, "then" *(entonces)*, "nowadays" *(hoy dia)*, "in the future" *(en el futuro)*, and "finally, or, at the end" *(al final)*.

How You Can Recognize Compare and Contrast Order

Comparing is telling how things are similar or alike. Contrasting is telling how things are different. On your *REALIDADES* test or your FCAT test, you may be asked to compare and contrast situations, settings, events, characters, plot, ideas, points of view, problems, or conclusions. When you are comparing things, you may use words like "also" *(también)*, "both" *(ambos, ambas)*, "likewise" *(igualmente)*, "similar" *(similar, similares)*, "but also" *(pero también)*, and "the same as" *(igual como, lo mismo)*. When you are contrasting things, you may use words like "however" *(sin embargo)*, "different from" *(diferente de)*, "on the contrary" *(al contrario)*, "on the other hand" *(por otra parte, por otro lado)*, "different" *(diferente)*, and *"but" (pero)*.

How You Can Recognize a Cause and Effect Order

An event, situation, or action that happens is a cause. An event, situation, or action that happens as a result of the cause is an effect. Here is an easy way to remember the difference between a cause and effect. If you can start the sentence and say, "Because this happened (cause), the result is that (effect)." For a cause, you may see words in English and Spanish like *"because" (porque)*, "due to" *(debido a)*, and "for this reason" *(por eso)*. For an effect, you may see words like "as a result" *(como resultado)*, "therefore" *(por lo tanto, entonces)*, "this caused" *(esto causó)*, "for this reason" *(por esta razón)*, "then" *(entonces)*, "finally" *(por fin, finalmente)*, and "so" *(entonces, pues)*.

How You Can Recognize Listing Order

The important details are listed in descriptive or expository readings. These readings include lists, and are sometimes adjectives. You may see words in English and Spanish, such as "tall" *(alto/a)*, "rich" *(rico/a)*, "long" *(largo/a)*, "dirty" *(sucio/a)*, or "unbelievable" *(increíble)*, "generous" *(generoso/a)*, and "old" *(viejo/a)*.

How You Can Recognize Geographic and Directional Order

The details are arranged in geographic or directional order. Directional words such as "up" *(arriba)*, "down" *(abajo)*, "behind" *(atras)*, "to the left" *(a la izquierda)*, "to the right" *(a la derecha)*, "next to" *(al lado de)*, "far from" *(lejos de)*, "close to" *(cerca de)*, and "on top of" *(encima de)* are used in directional order.

How You Can Find the Author's Purpose

The author's purpose is his/her reason for writing the passage: to tell a story, to entertain, to explain or illustrate, to demonstrate, to persuade, to describe, to expand your knowledge, or to express an opinion. In fiction (novels, short stories, and poems), look at the characters and their viewpoints or attitudes toward the subject. In nonfiction passages (biographies, autobiographies, journal entries, diaries, letters, interviews, surveys, editorials, and historical accounts) look at the explanations and descriptions. In persuasive writings, look at the opinions or viewpoints expressed in the passage.

How You Can Figure Out the Meanings of Words

You can figure out the meaning of an unfamiliar word by context clues. Context clues are the words, phrases, and sentences that come before or after the unknown word. This surrounding information gives you clues or ideas as to the meaning of the word. Another strategy to use is to figure out a word's meaning by looking at the prefixes (parts of the word added to the beginning) or suffixes (a letter or group of letters added to the end) of the word. Try to learn some common prefixes and suffixes before you take the FCAT.

Can You Recognize Clues about Characters, Plot, Tone, and Setting?

Here are some secret strategies for understanding characters, plot, tone, and setting.

How You Can Recognize Clues About the Characters and Plot

Understand what the main character wants, what he or she thinks, and why a character does what he or she does. Recognize what a character is like by how he or she is described. Ask yourself these questions: Is he or she honest (*honesto/a*), intelligent (*inteligente*), mischievous (*travieso/a*), or is he or she meek, kind (*amable*), or humble (*humilde*)? What is his or her personal background (*como era de niño/a*)? How does he or she relate with the other characters in the story? What does the character say?

Do you know that the plot includes several elements? These elements include: exposition or the background information, the rising action where the characters try to solve a problem, the climax or when the characters reach a very vital moment, the falling action where you see the consequences of the actions and finally the resolution to the problem in the story.

How You Can Recognize the Tone of the Reading Passage

The tone of the passage is how the author feels or his or her attitude toward a particular subject. Look at the adjectives or descriptions, actions, and repeated words. Ask yourself, "Is the tone sad (*triste*), happy (*alegre, contento*), peaceful (*tranquilo*), or fun (*divertido*)?

How You Can Recognize the Setting of the Reading Passage

The setting of the passage is where the story takes place, its atmosphere, and the time in which it takes place. Does it take place today, many years ago (*hace muchos años*), in a city (*en la ciudad*), or in an old Spanish village (*en un pueblo antiguo español*), on a space ship (*en una nave espacial*), or in a Latin American high school (*en una escuela secundaria de Latinoamérica*)?

Getting Started

So, let's get started. If there was anything in this "To the Student" Introduction that you did not understand, ask your teacher about it. Glance once again at the secret strategies before completing this FCAT Support section. In fact, it will be helpful if you review those strategies each time you take one of these tests. And remember: The more you practice, the higher your scores will be.

¡Buena suerte!

Strategies to Analyze Words: Context and Word Structure Clues

It is impossible to know the meaning of every word in a language. Good readers develop strategies to determine the meanings of unknown words in their reading without having to look them up in the dictionary. Good readers also know that their guesses may be wrong, so they develop strategies to check their guesses. Then, they use more traditional methods of finding the word's meaning: looking it up in the dictionary or asking for assistance from someone trustworthy.

 Tip

Knowing the English equivalent of common Spanish suffixes can help you build your vocabulary both in English and Spanish. For example, page 52 of your textbook features the section **Exploración del lenguaje,** about Spanish diminutives. The suffix *-ito* or *-ita* in a Spanish word can be used to show affection for that particular person or thing, or it can be used to indicate that the person or thing is little or small in size. Likewise, in English, the suffix *-ette* can indicate that a person or thing is little or small in size; the suffixes *-y* or *-ie* can be used to show affection for a person or thing.

You must be aware that just because an English word ends with *-ette*, *-y*, or *-ie*, does not mean that the suffixes can always translate to a term of affection or to something small. When making an educated guess about an unusual word, you should will always test your guess in context. In other words, you should insert your guessed meaning into the actual sentence where you found the unusual word.

1. Read the following sentence: When I am with my <u>sweetie</u>, the days always seem <u>rosy</u>. Only one of the underlined words uses the *-ie* or *-y* suffix as a term of affection. Which one is it? Now read this sentence: "The artist hardly needed any paint from his <u>palette</u> to paint the <u>statuette</u>." Only one of the underlined words uses the *-ette* suffix to indicate something small in size? Which one is it?

Sample FCAT question:

2. Read the passage below and answer the question that follows.

Fred's mom is blond, and his aunt is <u>brunette</u>. Fred loves his aunt, and she is crazy about him. "Come visit me, <u>Freddy</u>!" she'll often say over the telephone. Whenever Fred visits her in her small apartment, she always has a special <u>chocolatey</u> treat waiting for him in her <u>kitchenette</u>.

Based on your understanding of the underlined words in the passage, which statement below is TRUE?
A Fred's aunt is short with brown hair.
B Freddy is small in size.
C "Chocolatey" is a term of affection.
D The aunt's kitchen is small in size.

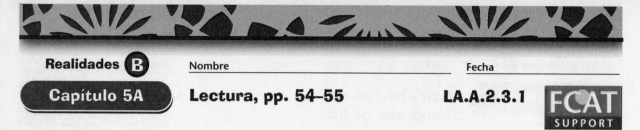

Determining the Main Idea and Identifying Relevant Details

To know the relevant details in a reading passage is to know which ones are most important. The first step in identifying the relevant details is to identify the main idea of the passage. The relevant details are the ones that help support the main idea. After reading a passage, good readers ask themselves, "What is this passage mostly about?" and "Which details in the passage help support, explain, or prove the main idea?"

Tip

Some readers are better able to identify the main idea and the relevant details when they have a graphic organizer. The graphic organizer below is a cluster or a web where the main idea is the central circle and the relevant details sprout out from the center like spokes on a wheel.

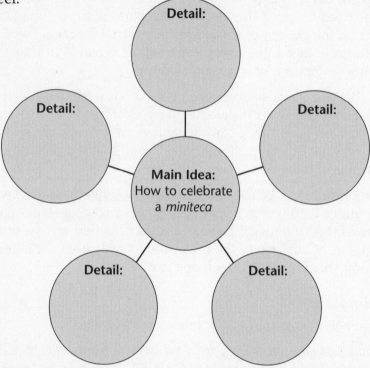

1. On pages 54–55 in your textbook, re-read the **Lectura, ¡Te invitamos a nuestra miniteca!** The main idea of this passage is about how to celebrate a special occasion with a *miniteca*. Use the cluster graphic organizer above to list any relevant details in the passage that show the features of a *miniteca* celebration.

Sample FCAT question:

2. Which is NOT one of the relevant details featured in the **Lectura** about celebrating a special occasion with a *miniteca*?
   A Guests pay a small fee to attend.
   B It can be celebrated at a house or at a special location.
   C Lights, decorations, and music help create a festive atmosphere.
   D Parents spend time with the young people.

Realidades B

Capítulo 5A

LA.A.2.3.5, LA.A.2.3.2,
LA.A.2.2.7, LA.A.1.3.2

Holidays in the Hispanic World

1 Some holidays are celebrated differently in Latin America and Spain than in the United States. *La Nochebuena,* or Christmas Eve, for example, is when most of the Spanish-speaking world celebrates Christmas. A nativity scene (*un nacimiento* or *un pesebre*) is a common decoration in homes. It may be small—the Dominican Republic is famous for its truly miniature figures—or large enough to fill an entire room or patio. But large or small, it is often very elaborate, with hills, trees, roads, little houses, and small mirrors to represent ponds. *El nacimiento* is usually the focal point of the festivities, with family gathered around to sing carols to the accompaniment of a guitar or a bamboo pipe or maracas. Colored paper lanterns, balloons, piñatas, and dancing are often part of the evening celebration.

2 Epiphany (*el Día de los Reyes*), on January 6, marks the formal end of the Christmas holidays. Traditionally, it was the day on which children in Spanish-speaking countries received their gifts, because it commemorates the arrival of the Three Kings into Bethlehem with their gifts of gold, frankincense, and myrrh. Today, however, in more and more homes, gifts are opened on Christmas Day or on Christmas Eve.

3 In much of Latin America, the weather is warm during the end-of-year holidays (below the equator it is the beginning of summer) and *el Año Nuevo* may be celebrated with fireworks and even barbecues. In Spain, it is the custom to eat twelve grapes at the stroke of midnight, one grape each time the clock chimes.

4 *El Día de la Raza,* October 12, celebrates the blending of the Spanish and indigenous cultures that resulted from Columbus's landing in the Americas. It is sometimes called *el Día de la Hispanidad.* In recent years, however, it has become of less importance than specific national holidays. *El Día de la Independencia* is, of course, celebrated on different days in different countries. For example, September 15 is the national holiday of four Central American nations: Guatemala, Honduras, El Salvador, and Nicaragua. Paraguay celebrates its independence from Spain on May 14; Argentina, May 25; Venezuela, July 5; Colombia, July 20; Peru, July 28; Bolivia, August 6; Ecuador, August 10; Mexico, September 16; and Chile and Costa Rica, September 18. The Dominican Republic celebrates its independence from Haiti on February 27; Uruguay, its independence from Brazil on August 25; Panama, its independence from Colombia on November 3. And Spain's national holiday? *El Día de la Hispanidad*—October 12.

FCAT
TEST PRACTICE

Holidays in the Hispanic World (*continued*)

5 Another major fall holiday is *el Día de los Muertos* (All Souls' Day) on November 2. This holiday is a day of remembrance for all those who have died. It is a very special celebration in Mexico. There are, of course, prayers, religious services, and visits to the cemetery. Families build special altars, called *ofrendas*, in their homes. These *ofrendas* are decorated with flowers and candles, but they are not at all solemn. Photographs of loved ones who have died are displayed among objects that they cherished or used most—a rocking chair, for example, or reading glasses, gardening tools, or cooking utensils. *El Día de los Muertos* is also celebrated by eating a sweetened

bread—*el pan de muerto*—which is either shaped like skulls and crosses, or decorated with white sugar candies in the shape of skulls, crosses, coffins, and tombs. For children, there are white masks, tin or wire skeletons attached to strings, and even toy coffins that contain a skeleton that jumps out when a string is pulled.

6 In the calendar of the Catholic Church, almost every day is dedicated to one or more saints. A person's "saint's day," or *santo*, is the day dedicated to the saint who has that person's name (or one derived from it). For example, *el santo* for every José, Josefina, or Josefa is St. Joseph's Day (March 19), and *el santo* for every Pablo, Paulo, Paulina, and Paula is St. Paul's Day (June 29). Traditionally, part of a person's name was determined by the saint's day on which he or she was born. For example, if a girl whose family planned to name her María Luisa happened to be born on May 30—St. Ferdinand's Day—she would likely be named María Luisa Fernanda to honor that saint. In fact, the traditional Mexican "Happy Birthday" song, *Las mañanitas*, is actually a song for a saint's day.

7 This custom is disappearing, however, and a person's birthday and saint's day are often not the same. In many countries, a person's saint's day is considered more important than a birthday. Even non-Catholics may celebrate their *santo*, for no one wants to miss out on his or her special day for a party and a few gifts. So truly every day is *un día de fiesta en el mundo hispano!*

Realidades B

Capítulo 5A

**LA.A.2.3.5, LA.A.2.3.2,
LA.A.2.2.7, LA.A.1.3.2**

FCAT
TEST PRACTICE

Answer questions 1–5. Base your answers on the reading *"Holidays in the Hispanic World."*

1 Which of the following statements is NOT true?

   A *El Día de los Muertos* on November 2nd is known as *All Souls' Day* in English.

   B On *el Día de los Muertos*, altars are decorated with flowers and candles.

   C On *el Día de los Muertos,* people eat sweet bread called *el pan de muerto.*

   D Only those who have died within the past year are remembered on *el Día de los Muertos.*

2 What is the author's purpose for writing this article?

   F to explain, describe, and at times compare the important holidays in Latin America with those in the United States

   G to state his or her opinion of why Latin Americans celebrate their holidays

   H to persuade the readers that they should celebrate Latin American holidays

   I to convince the readers that the people in the United States should learn about Latin American holidays

3 The words *el Año Nuevo* mean:

   A Independence Day

   B the New Year

   C All Souls' Day

   D Saint's Day

4 Which of the following statements is true?

   F All of the nations of Central America have the same Independence Day.

   G In the United States, the best-known national holiday among the Latin American nations is *el Día de los Reyes.*

   H Of the nations of Latin America, all but two celebrate their national holiday within the five-month period from May to September.

   I All of the Spanish-speaking countries of Latin America got their independence from Spain.

5 READ THINK EXPLAIN   Compare and contrast Latin American holidays with those in the United States. Use details and information from the article to support your answer.

Nombre _____ Fecha _____

Answer Sheet

1 Ⓐ Ⓑ Ⓒ Ⓓ   **2** Ⓕ Ⓖ Ⓗ Ⓘ   **3** Ⓐ Ⓑ Ⓒ Ⓓ

4 Ⓕ Ⓖ Ⓗ Ⓘ

5

READ
THINK
EXPLAIN

_____

_____

_____

_____

_____

_____

_____

_____

Realidades B

Capítulo 5B

Nombre

Fecha

Conexiones, p. 81

LA.A.2.3.1

FCAT
SUPPORT

Identifying Methods of Development and Patterns of Organization

Good readers understand the tools and techniques of authors. To identify the methods of development used by an author in a text, good readers must first determine the author's purpose by asking, "Why was this text written?" After determining the author's purpose, readers next ask, "What techniques did the author use to achieve his or her purpose?" These techniques are known as methods of development and could include, among other things, the organization pattern, the word choice, or the sentence structure used in the text.

Tip

One common pattern of organization for writers is the process paper. The process paper could be a set of instructions, a recipe, a "how-to" guide, or even the summary of a story. In a process paper, you explain the steps in a process. A graphic organizer known as a flow chart helps you keep track of all those steps. The flow chart also helps you see which steps come first in the process and which ones follow.

1. After re-reading the recipe for *Arroz con leche* in **Actividad 25 "Un postre delicioso"** on page 81 in your textbook, fill in the recipe steps in the flow chart below.

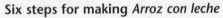
Six steps for making *Arroz con leche*

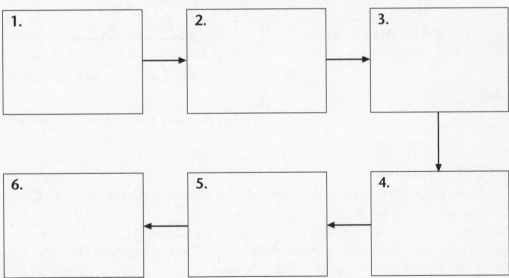

Sample FCAT question:

2. According to the recipe for *Arroz con leche,* when should the cook add the sugar and vanilla to the rice?

    A Before cooking it slowly for one hour.

    B After putting it in the refrigerator.

    C After cooking it slowly for one hour.

    D While soaking the rice for one hour and a half.

Realidades **B**

Capítulo 5B

Nombre

Lectura, p. 84

Fecha

LA.A.1.3.2

FCAT
SUPPORT

Making and Confirming Inferences

One indication of good readers is their ability to read between the lines of a text. Not only do they literally read and comprehend what a text says, but they also make inferences from what they read. An inference is an educated guess about something written in the text. An inference, because it is a guess, can never be absolutely right or wrong. However, an inference, like a conclusion, can be believable based upon the evidence that is present in the text. Confirming an inference means locating the evidence in the text that lends support to the inference.

Tip

One strategy that helps students as they make and confirm inferences is a two-column note activity known as Opinion-Proof. As you read, you formulate educated guesses or opinions about what you have read. Jot these down on the Opinion side of your notes. If your opinions are believable, then you should be able to write down on the Proof side all the evidence you find in the reading passage that lends support to your opinion or inference.

1. On page 84 in your textbook, read the **Lectura, *Una visita a Santa Fe.*** Based on what you have read, fill in the missing blanks of the Opinion-Proof chart below.

Opinion	Proof
Alicia and Pedro are good cousins to Rosario and Luis.	_____
	_____
_____	*¡No sabemos bailar pero va a ser muy divertido!*
_____	*¡Los cinco días van a pasar rápidamente!*

Sample FCAT question:

2. Based on the information presented in the letter from Alicia and Pedro to Rosario and Luis, the reader can infer that
   A Santa Fe is a city with over 400 years of history and culture.
   B Rosario and Luis will likely be bored during their visit to Santa Fe.
   C Alicia and Pedro are not easily embarrassed.
   D the *fandango* is a dance better known for its excitement than for its history.

EL SOL, viernes 18 de julio

NOTICIAS DE CELEBRACIONES

Esta semana en San Antonio muchas familias celebran ocasiones muy especiales.

Quinceañera

Mirella Lugo Armas, hija de Humberto Lugo Díaz y Carmen Armas Garza de Lugo, celebra sus quince años el domingo 20 de julio a las 6:00 P.M. en el restaurante Casa Estrella. Hay una gran fiesta con una banda de música tejana después de la cena.

Boda

Dolores Lara Villarreal y Roberto Pastor Peña celebran su boda en la iglesia de San Antonio, el sábado 19 de julio a las 8:00 P.M. Después de la ceremonia hay una fiesta con música y una cena en casa de la familia Lara.

Día del santo

Santiago Paredes Sánchez celebra el día de su santo el viernes 25 de julio. Hay una comida en su honor en casa de sus abuelos a las 2:00 P.M.

Graduación

Ana Luisa Martínez Puente celebra su graduación de la Memorial High School el día 22 de julio. Después de la graduación hay una barbacoa para la familia y los amigos en el parque Fiesta Texas a las 4:00 P.M.

Cincuenta años

Roberto González Juárez y María Luisa Gallardo Correa de González celebran su aniversario de bodas el 25 de julio en el salón de fiestas La Suerte. Van a celebrar la ocasión con una comida deliciosa para la familia y los amigos.

Answer questions 1–5. Base your answers on the article *"Noticias de celebraciones."*

1 According to the author, which of the celebrations has a party outdoors?

A *cincuenta años*

B *graduación*

C *día del santo*

D *quinceañera*

2 The information in this article could be MOST likely seen in

F the obituaries.

G the social pages.

H an advertisment.

I the school newspaper.

3 Which of the celebrations mentions the names of the parents of the honored person or people?

A *graduación*

B *quinceañera*

C *día del santo*

D *boda*

4 According to this article, which statement is true?

F Mirella Lugo Armas is going to have her "Sweet Fifteen" birthday party on Sunday, July 20th.

G Roberto González Juárez and María Luisa Gallardo Correa de González are celebrating their wedding anniversary on July 25th.

H Santiago Paredes Sánchez is celebrating his saint's day (birthday) on June 25th.

I Dolores Lara Villareal and Roberto Pastor Peña are celebrating their wedding anniversary on July 19th.

5 If you were going to have a birthday party for your friend, José Félix Sanchez González, born on July 20th, and wanted to write an announcement for the newspaper, what would you write? Support your answer with information or details from the article.

Nombre _____

Fecha _____

Answer Sheet

FCAT
TEST PRACTICE

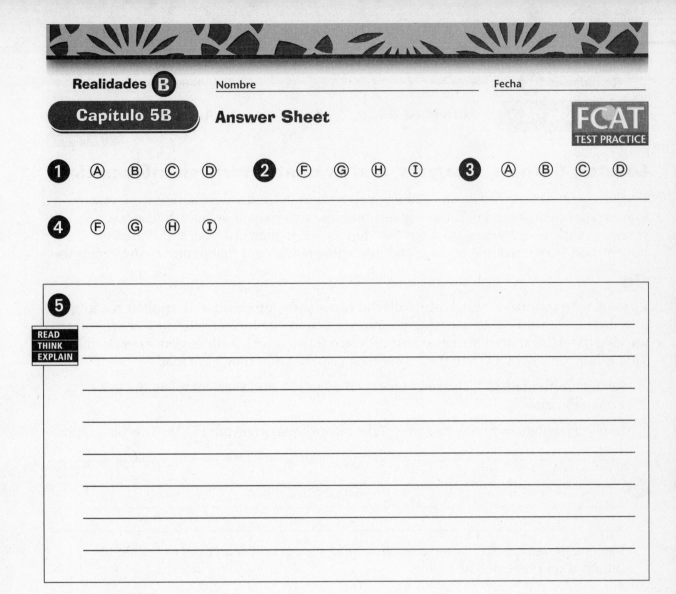

1 Ⓐ Ⓑ Ⓒ Ⓓ   **2** Ⓕ Ⓖ Ⓗ Ⓘ   **3** Ⓐ Ⓑ Ⓒ Ⓓ

4 Ⓕ Ⓖ Ⓗ Ⓘ

5

READ
THINK
EXPLAIN

_____

_____

_____

_____

_____

_____

_____

_____

Realidades B

Capítulo 6A

Nombre

Fecha

Actividad 33, p. 114

LA.A.2.3.5

Locates, Gathers, Analyzes, and Evaluates Written Information

By showing that they can locate, gather, analyze, and evaluate information from one or more reading passages, good readers demonstrate that they know how to conduct research. On a test, readers are often asked to locate, gather, analyze, and evaluate information from a reading passage and then show how to put that information to good use.

Tip

Readers who conduct research are skilled at translating information from their reading into their own words. If they encounter information in one format, such as a chart, they are able to restate that information in a different format, such as in sentences or as bullets. This is how they demonstrate their comprehension of what they have read.

1. Review **Actividad 33** "*¿Duermes bien?*" on page 114, and then complete the two exercises below.

   Use four sentences to restate some of the information presented in the two pie graphs.

   _____

   _____

   _____

   _____

   Use one paragraph with a topic sentence and supporting sentences to restate the information presented as bullets.

   _____

   _____

   _____

   _____

   _____

   _____

   _____

Sample FCAT question:

2. Imagine that a friend was sleeping only 5–6 hours on school nights. Which information from the graphs and bullets in **Actividad 33** would be LEAST likely to make your friend start sleeping more?

   A Las personas que duermen menos de seis horas por noche sufren más lesiones.

   B 52% de las personas duermen ocho horas o más en los fines de la semana.

   C Las personas que duermen menos de seis horas por noche tienen más problemas de relaciones interpersonales.

   D Solamente 15% de las personas duermen menos de seis horas durante la semana.

Understanding Tone

To understand an author's tone in a reading passage, good readers focus not just on what is said, but also on how it is said. Like identifying an author's point of view, identifying an author's tone requires readers to ask, "What is the author's attitude or feelings about the subject of the reading passage?" First, readers should be able to identify when an author feels positive, negative, or neutral toward a subject. As readers gain more practice with this skill, they should be able to identify a wide range of tones used by authors. Some of these might include: admiration, nostalgia, objectivity, sarcasm, surprise, and sympathy.

Tip

One way to begin to understand an author's tone is to separate the statements of fact from the statements of opinion. While statements of fact make an author seem more objective, statements of opinion often express the author's feelings about a subject.

1. After reviewing the **Lectura**, *El desastre en mi dormitorio* on pages 116–117 in your textbook, identify the statements from the reading passage as facts or opinions. Then, for each opinion, identify the feelings that it reveals about the author.

	Fact or Opinion	Feelings Expressed by Opinions
Rosario: *"Estoy desesperada."*	_____	_____
Rosario: *"Hay pizza debajo de la cama."*	_____	_____
Rosario: *"[Negro] es el peor color y es feísimo."*	_____	_____
Magdalena: *"Uds. son muy diferentes."*	_____	_____
Magdalena: *"Ella cree que el color negro es el más bonito."*	_____	_____

Sample FCAT question:

2. How does the tone expressed in Rosario's letter compare to the tone expressed in Magdalena's letter?

   A Rosario seems more helpful than Magdalena.

   B Magdalena seems more exaggerated than Rosario.

   C Both Rosario and Magdalena have an angry tone in their letters.

   D Magdalena seems more objective than Rosario.

How "Spanish" Is *Spanish* Architecture?

1 If you were to travel from the southwestern United States to the southern tip of South America, many buildings would look fairly familiar almost every place you visited. Although regional differences would be obvious, you would still be aware of a certain look shared by many communities in the southwestern United States and Latin America. In large part, that look can be traced to the architecture of Moorish Spain.

2 The Moors were North African Arabs who ruled most of the Iberian Peninsula (Spain and Portugal) for nearly 800 years—from the early eighth century until the late fifteenth century. Many elements of Latin American architecture were first introduced to Spain by the Moors during that period.

3 Patios, for example, became common in cities such as Córdoba and Sevilla beginning in the early eleventh century.

Because of widespread political and social unrest during that time, houses were built with heavy doors and thick, fortress-like walls. These walls also helped shield the rooms inside from the sun's heat. The patios, placed in the center of the house and accessible from all first-floor rooms, often had tiled floors. In the center, surrounded by lemon trees and flowers, there was often a pool or a large clay pot filled with cool water. Patios were thus probably the first naturally "air-conditioned" rooms. Throughout Latin America today, as well as in Spain, central patios are still a popular feature of many commercial buildings as well as homes.

4 Another common element of Latin American architecture is the *balcón*, or *mirador*. In Moorish Spain, homes typically had balconies off the second-floor sleeping areas. These balconies, which often included intricately designed wrought iron railings and grates, overlooked the patio. During the period when Latin America was being

colonized by Spain, balconies became common in Latin America as well. There was, however, a major difference: most Latin American balconies do not overlook the patio. Instead, they face outward so that people can view the street life of the town.

5 Buildings in Moorish Spain usually differed from those in northern Europe in another way as well. Although wood was used as a building material, it was not nearly as common as stone, brick, and adobe (heavy clay bricks made of sun-dried earth and straw). Today, builders in Latin America and the southwestern United States continue to use many of these same materials and techniques first introduced by the Moors.

Realidades B

Capítulo 6A

LA.A.2.2.7, LA.A.1.3.2

FCAT
TEST PRACTICE

Answer questions 1–5. Base your answers on the article *"How 'Spanish' is Spanish Architecture?"*

1 In the following excerpt, what does the word *mirador* mean?

> Another common element of Latin American architecture is the *balcón*, or *mirador*.

A architecture

B adobe material

C balcony

D heavy door

2 According to this article, what can we say about *Spanish* architecture?

F Buildings in Moorish Spain usually had air-conditioned rooms.

G Southwestern United States and Latin American architecture can be traced back to the Moors or North African Arabs.

H Spanish patios were used as a place to dry straw and clay bricks.

I Builders in the southwestern United States and Latin America no longer use the same materials and techniques introduced by the Moors.

3 According to the article, what was the main reason why the doors and walls of Spanish homes were so thick during the time of Moorish rule?

A They kept the house warm.

B They were used for defense and protection.

C They enclosed the patio.

D The Moors were used to living in homes with thick walls.

4 Why do architectural features that date to the period of Moorish influence in Spain exist in the southwestern United States and Latin America today?

F It gets very hot in those regions.

G Those regions were conquered by the Moors.

H Those regions were colonized by the Spanish.

I There is much political and social unrest in those regions.

5 READ THINK EXPLAIN Compare and contrast Latin American architecture with the architecture of Moorish Spain.

Realidades

Nombre _____   Fecha _____

Capítulo 6A   **Answer Sheet**

 FCAT TEST PRACTICE

1 Ⓐ Ⓑ Ⓒ Ⓓ   **2** Ⓕ Ⓖ Ⓗ Ⓘ   **3** Ⓐ Ⓑ Ⓒ Ⓓ

4 Ⓕ Ⓖ Ⓗ Ⓘ

5

READ
THINK
EXPLAIN

_____

_____

_____

_____

_____

_____

_____

_____

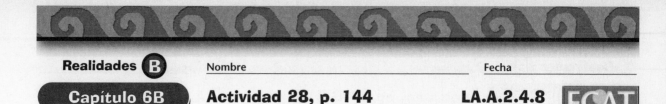

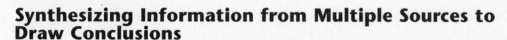

Synthesizing Information from Multiple Sources to Draw Conclusions

Often readers are asked to look at two or more reading passages and make connections between the different passages. When readers synthesize information, they are forming new ideas based on what they have read in the different reading passages.

Tip

When synthesizing information from various sources, readers benefit when they read actively. While they read, active readers are constantly formulating ideas about how information from various sources relate to each other. Active readers often show these relationships in charts, tables, or graphs.

1. Review **Actividad 28, "¿Qué casa están buscando?"** on page 144 in your textbook, and then fill out the chart below.

	What would the house buyer like about Casa Venezia?	*What would the house buyer dislike about Casa Venezia?*
José Guzmán		
Alejandro Lara		
Dora Peña		

Sample FCAT question:

2. Based on the descriptions about the three house buyers and the description of Casa Venezia, which statement below is true?

   A José Guzmán's wife would not like the kitchen at Casa Venezia.
   B Alejandro Lara needs a house like Casa Venezia with its three levels.
   C Dora Peña would have no need for Casa Venezia's carpets in the bedrooms.
   D Casa Venezia seems more suitable for Dora Peña than it does for José Guzmán.

Realidades B

Capítulo 6B

Nombre _____

Fecha _____

Lectura, pp. 146–147

LA.E.2.3.1

FCAT
SUPPORT

Analyzing the Effectiveness of Complex Elements of Plot

When reading stories, it is important for readers to identify the protagonist, or main character, of the story. The protagonist usually has a goal in the story, and it is the protagonist's attempt to reach that goal that moves along the plot of the story. The plot can be summed up as all the actions that occur as the protagonist attempts to reach his or her goal. While attempting to reach his or her goal, the protagonist encounters problems or conflicts that must be resolved. The climax of the story is the point when it becomes clear to the reader that the protagonist will or will not reach his or her goal. Good readers can explain how various elements of the plot such as the protagonist's goals or conflicts affect the outcome of the story.

Tip

1. One way you can identify and understand various plot elements is to use a chart. After reviewing the **Lectura,** *Cantaclara* on pages 146 and 147 in your textbook, fill in the information required in the chart below.

Who is the protagonist?
_____
_____
_____
_____

What is his/her goal?
_____
_____
_____
_____

What conflicts does he/she encounter?
_____
_____
_____
_____

What is the outcome of each conflict?
_____
_____
_____
_____

When is the climax of the story?
_____
_____
_____
_____

Sample FCAT question:

2. How would the outcome of the story have been different if Cantaclara had a nice stepmother but a poor singing voice?

   A Cantaclara would have had to let her sisters go with her to *La estrella del futuro*.

   B Cantaclara would have had to clean the kitchen before going to *La estrella del futuro*, but she would not have been a winner.

   C Cantaclara would not have had to clean the kitchen, but she would not have been a winner on *La estrella del futuro*.

   D Cantaclara's mother would have introduced Cantaclara to a handsome prince who would have told Cantaclara that he loved her even without a beautiful singing voice.

FCAT TEST PRACTICE

Mi segunda casa es … ¡una cueva!

1 ¡Hola! Me llamo Macarena y soy española. Vivo con mis padres y tres hermanos en un apartamento grande y bonito en Granada, que está en el sur de España. Pero tenemos otra casa y es… ¡una cueva! Nuestra casa-cueva está cerca de Guadix, un pueblo pintoresco de unos 20.000 habitantes. Guadix está a 60 kilómetros de Granada, y es famoso por sus casas-cueva.

2 Más de un cuarto de la población del pueblo vive en estas casas subterráneas. Tradicionalmente sólo para los pobres y artesanos, hoy día las casas-cueva son la segunda residencia de muchas familias de la clase media. ¡Me encanta pasar tiempo con mi familia en nuestra casa-cueva!

3 ¿Qué tienen de atractivo las casas-cueva?

- La temperatura se mantiene constante (20 grados centígrados) durante todo el año.
- Si la familia necesita más espacio, sólo hay que excavar otro cuarto.

- Tienen todas las comodidades de una casa moderna: dormitorios, cocina, cuarto de baño, sala, comedor, chimenea, electricidad y conexiones para Internet y fax.
- De la puerta hay una magnífica vista. (¡Pocas cuevas tienen ventanas!)

4 Si quieres vivir en un <u>ambiente</u> original, íntimo y rústico, o si simplemente prefieres vivir en otra casa durante el fin de semana o durante las vacaciones de verano, las casas-cueva son perfectas para ti.

Una casa en el Barrio de las cuevas

España

Granada
Guadix

Answer questions 1–5. Base your answers on the article, *"Mi segunda casa es . . . ¡una cueva!"*

1   According to the author, how is a "cave house" similar to a modern house?

A   Both have doors, windows, bedrooms, a kitchen, a bathroom, a living room, a playroom, and a dining room.

B   Both have electricity, bedrooms, a kitchen, a bathroom, a living room, a dining room, and a fireplace.

C   Both have spectacular views of the mountains, doors, windows, and an office.

D   Both have bedrooms, two floors, doors, windows, bedrooms, a kitchen, a bathroom, a living room, and a dining room.

2   In the sentence, *"Si quieres vivir en un <u>ambiente</u> original, íntimo y rústico, o si simplemente prefieres vivir en otra casa durante el fin de semana o durante las vacaciones de verano, las casas-cueva son perfectas para ti,"* what does the word *ambiente* mean?

F   countryside

G   cave

H   atmosphere

I   city

3   According to the author, what is one of the reasons why Macarena likes spending time at her "cave house"?

A   The temperature maintains itself at a constant 20 degrees centigrade during the summer.

B   The temperature maintains itself at 20 degrees centigrade all year long.

C   If the family needs space, they can always just set up a tent in the extra space.

D   She can see a magnificent view from her bedroom window.

4   According to the author, which of the following statements is false?

F   Cave houses have all the conveniences of a modern home.

G   Cave houses are not only for artisans and the poor.

H   Macarena's family has two homes.

I   Cave houses offer beautiful views from the windows.

5   READ THINK EXPLAIN   What was the author's purpose for writing this article? Use details and information from the article to support your answer.

Nombre _____ Fecha _____

Answer Sheet

1 Ⓐ Ⓑ Ⓒ Ⓓ   **2** Ⓕ Ⓖ Ⓗ Ⓘ   **3** Ⓐ Ⓑ Ⓒ Ⓓ

4 Ⓕ Ⓖ Ⓗ Ⓘ

5

READ
THINK
EXPLAIN

_____

_____

_____

_____

_____

_____

_____

_____

Interpreting Diagrams, Graphs, and Statistical Illustrations

When good readers encounter a diagram, a graph, or any statistical information, they are able to make meaning from what they see. They are able to translate the information that is presented graphically or statistically into useful information. Readers are often asked to make comparisons involving the information in the diagrams, graphs, or statistics.

Tip

One strategy that helps students make meaning from diagrams, graphs, and statistics is to practice translating graphic or statistical information into sentences. In describing relationships that you observe in the diagrams, graphs, or statistics, you should become familiar with making statements with the following words or expressions of comparison:

more than ➔ most   less than ➔ least ➔ fewer than
greater than ➔ larger ➔ largest   smaller ➔ smallest
bigger ➔ biggest   equal ➔ same ➔ different

1. Review **Actividad 10** on page 165 in your textbook. Look at the foreign currency exchange rate data below and then answer the questions that follow.

Foreign Exchange Rates Compared to the U.S. Dollar

Country	Currency	$1 U.S. =	Country	Currency	$1 U.S. =
Argentina	peso	3.0050	Peru	nuevo sol	3.414
Colombia	peso	2274.50	Uruguay	nuevo peso	24.4350
Mexico	peso	10.4730	Venezuela	bolivar	2147.30

Would the shoes in **Actividad 12** that cost 1,820 Uruguayan pesos cost more or less in U.S. dollars? Why?

_____

Are 1,820 Uruguayan pesos worth more or less than 1,820 Mexican pesos? Why?

_____

Which peso (from Argentina, Colombia, Mexico, or Uruguay) could be purchased with the smallest amount of U.S. currency? Why?

_____

Sample FCAT question:

2. Based on the information presented in the Foreign Exchange Rate chart above, which statement below is true?
   A When exchanging for U.S. dollars, the Uruguayan nuevo peso is nearly equal in value to the Colombian peso.
   B The number of pesos you would receive in Mexico for 10 U.S. dollars is more than the number of pesos you would receive in Argentina for the same amount of U.S. dollars.
   C One Venezuelan bolivar is equal to 2147.30 U.S. dollars.
   D You would need more Argentinian pesos than Peruvian nuevo soles to buy $1 U.S. dollar.

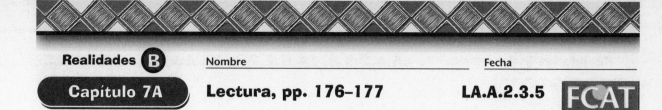

Realidades **B**

Capítulo 7A

Nombre _____

Fecha _____

Lectura, pp. 176–177

LA.A.2.3.5

FCAT
SUPPORT

Locates, Gathers, Analyzes, and Evaluates Written Information

By showing that they can locate, gather, analyze, and evaluate information from one or more reading passages, good readers demonstrate that they know how to conduct research. On a test, readers are often asked to locate, gather, analyze, and evaluate information from a reading passage and then show how to put that information to good use.

Tip

Readers who conduct research are skilled at organizing information from their reading. For many, the outline is an excellent way to organize information gathered from research. With an outline, you begin by organizing information into broad categories and then gradually narrow your focus to more specific details.

1. Review the **Lectura,** *Tradiciones de la ropa panameña* on pages 176 and 177 in your textbook and then fill in the missing blanks of the outline below.

Traditional Panamanian Clothing

I _____
 A *Montuna*
 B *De* _____
  1 _____
  2 It costs a lot.
   a _____
   b _____
   c _____
  3 Something that is very important in the city of Las Tablas.

II *La blusa de molas*
 A Made by the Kuna Indians from the San Blas Islands.
 B Molas are decorative panels on the fronts and backs of the blouses.
  1 _____
  2 _____
  3 *Molas* can be found in museums as works of art.

Sample FCAT question:

2. If you were interested in making your own samples of traditional Panamanian clothing, all of the following statements would be helpful to you EXCEPT which one?
 A You will need a lot of jewels to decorate a *pollera de gala*.
 B You can show your individual talent and expression with your *molas*.
 C You will discover that the *pollera de gala* is most important in the city of Las Tablas.
 D A *pollera de gala* could require as many as seven months to make by hand.

A Culture as Seen Through Its Textiles

1 On July 26, 1925, archaeologists made a dramatic discovery in the desert of the Paracas peninsula, approximately 150 miles south of the Peruvian capital of Lima. In the desert off the Pacific coast they found an underground network of tombs from the Paracas and Nazca cultures that dated back to the fourth century B.C. Such a group of elaborately interconnected tombs is sometimes called a necropolis, a Greek word meaning "city of the dead." The Paracas necropolis contained beautiful, richly decorated gold objects, along with hundreds of perfectly preserved human bodies carefully wrapped in intricately woven, embroidered cloth that was as well preserved as the bodies it contained.

2 Woven cloth, or textiles, has of course played both a practical and a ceremonial role in world cultures for thousands of years. The textiles found at Paracas were probably specially made for use in burials and almost surely revealed the social status of the people buried there.

3 Images woven into garments or added to them were a form of communication in ancient cultures. Whether painted, embroidered, or decorated with metal or brightly colored feathers, many textiles contained important symbolic information. The most common images found on the Paracas textiles were those of birds, cats, snakes, rodents, llamas, and fish. By showing the animals that were native to the region, these pictures represented in one way or another the three basic realms of nature that daily affected the people who made the pictures: the sky, the earth, and the sea. Human forms were also shown. These pictures no doubt reflected concepts important to the culture, such as nature gods, the individual's ancestors, or the individual's social status.

4 Today, people in Peru and neighboring Bolivia continue to weave ponchos, tunics, and hats that use some of the same designs found in their people's textiles over 2,000 years ago.

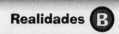

Answer questions 1–5. Base your answers on the reading, *"A Culture as Seen Through Its Textiles."*

1 According to the evidence in the article, the woven cloth, or textiles

   A probably were made for use in burials, revealed the social status of the people buried there, and preserved the bodies that were wrapped in them.

   B probably were used as a form of currency for wealthy people.

   C probably were used to communicate with the dead.

   D probably were used to please the dead.

2 According to the author, why were images included in the textiles of ancient peoples?

   F for purely religious reasons

   G to communicate information of some sort

   H to preserve the body of the person around whom it was wrapped

   I to impress visitors to the tombs

3 Which sentence best describes the main idea of the passage?

   A Through the images woven and embroidered onto ancient textiles, ancient cultures can be studied.

   B Through the network of tombs of the Paracas peninsula, scientists can now discover the styles of clothing that the ancient people wore.

   C The tombs of Paracas were just like the tombs of the ancient Greeks.

   D Human bodies can be preserved if they are wrapped in the proper types of textiles.

4 Why are the interconnected tombs of the Paracas peninsula called a necropolis?

   F Because Paracas is located near Greece.

   G Because necropolis is a Greek term referring to the "city of the dead".

   H Because there is no word in Spanish referring to the tombs.

   I Because the ancient Greeks settled in Paracas during the time the interconnected tombs were being built.

5 How did the images that were embroidered or decorated on the ancient textiles of Paracas contribute to communication in ancient cultures? Use specific information and details from the article to explain your answer.

Nombre _____

Fecha _____

Answer Sheet

1 Ⓐ Ⓑ Ⓒ Ⓓ　　**2** Ⓕ Ⓖ Ⓗ Ⓘ　　**3** Ⓐ Ⓑ Ⓒ Ⓓ

4 Ⓕ Ⓖ Ⓗ Ⓘ

5

READ
THINK
EXPLAIN

_____

_____

_____

_____

_____

_____

_____

_____

Realidades B

Capítulo 7B

Nombre _____

Fecha _____

Actividad 19, p. 200

LA.A.2.4.8

Drawing Conclusions

To draw a conclusion is to form an opinion based on evidence. Sometimes the evidence presented to readers is very limited, but they must ensure that their evidence-based opinions make sense.

Conclusion statements are rarely right or wrong. They are often presented as believable or not. If you are successful at drawing conclusions from your reading, then you likely are skilled at finding evidence in your reading that supports your conclusions.

Conclusions are only as strong as the evidence on which they are based. Conclusions based on little evidence are not as believable as conclusions based on a lot of different kinds of evidence. You must also be willing to change your conclusions as more evidence becomes available in the reading passage.

Tip

One strategy that helps students as they draw conclusions is to use "If-Then" statements with their evidence and conclusions. If a conclusion does not make logical sense, then it will become obvious when presented in an "If-Then" statement. As more evidence is presented in the "If" statements, the conclusions in the "Then" statements will also likely change.

1. On page 200 of your textbook, review **Actividad 19 "Una lección de historia,"** and then complete these statements. Can you draw more than one possible conclusion for the evidence presented below?

   A **If** in 1848 President James K. Polk paid $15 million dollars to Mexico according to the Treaty of Hidalgo, **and**

   B **If** in 1898 President William McKinley helped Cuba and Puerto Rico declare their independence from Spain, **then** one could conclude that

   _____

   or

   _____ .

   Now add this third piece of evidence:

   C **If** in 1904 President Theodore Roosevelt began building the Panama Canal, **then** based on points **A, B,** and **C,** one could conclude that American presidents

   _____

   _____ .

Sample FCAT question:

2. If Columbus discovered the Dominican Republic in 1492 and if Juan Ponce de León explored Florida in 1513, then one could conclude that

   A both Columbus and de León were motivated by the desire to find gold.

   B the Dominican Republic and Florida had a lot in common during the 1500's.

   C Spain was active in exploration of the Americas in the late fifteenth and early sixteenth centuries.

   D neither Columbus nor de León discovered the fountain of youth in the New World.

Determining Main Idea

To determine the main idea of a reading passage, the reader must be able to describe what a reading passage is mostly about. He or she should be able to summarize the main idea of the reading passage in one sentence. A common problem for students when working with this skill is confusing an important detail in the reading passage with the main idea. Just because something is mentioned in the reading passage does not mean it is the main idea of the passage. Many times the main idea is not even stated in the reading passage. This is often called an implied main idea. No matter if the main idea is stated or implied, the basic question remains the same: "What is this reading passage mostly about?"

Tip

One common mistake that students make with main-idea questions is that they often choose main-idea statements that are either too broad or too narrow. When you are too broad in your thinking, you are too general and do not recognize what is unique about the particular reading passage. When you are too narrow, you focus too much on isolated details without looking at the whole picture.

1. Review the **Lectura, ¡De compras!** on pages 208 and 209 of your textbook. Then read the main-idea statements listed below and indicate if they are too broad, too narrow, or just right.

    _____ Little Havana is the heart of the Cuban community in Miami.

    _____ Shopping is a fun activity.

    _____ United States cities with large Hispanic communities offer interesting shopping opportunities.

    _____ Hispanic residents of the United States love to go shopping.

    _____ Olvera Street is the oldest street in Los Angeles and the place to see Mexican culture.

    _____ One can find inexpensive and unique things to buy in the Hispanic neighborhoods of American cities.

Sample FCAT question:

2. Another good title for the reading passage "¡De compras!" would be
    A "Guava Paste on Miami's Eighth Street."
    B "Shopping Adventures in America's Hispanic Neighborhoods."
    C "Trying to Find Original Products at Good Prices."
    D "What to Buy in Los Angeles and San Antonio."

Necesito comprar ropa

¿Te gusta ir de compras, pero no te gusta estar con muchas personas?
Lee este artículo de la solución de Margarita para este problema.

1 Margarita, una joven argentina de dieciséis años, tiene un problema. Necesita comprar ropa para sus vacaciones en Chile, pero está muy ocupada. No le gusta ir al centro comercial porque siempre hay muchas personas por allí. Decide visitar uno de los sitios en el Internet para buscar la ropa que necesita.

2 Primero, Margarita busca un sitio donde se especializan en ropa para jóvenes. El sitio que más le gusta tiene un catálogo con mucha variedad de ropa moderna. En la página principal, hay información sobre cómo seleccionar el departamento donde quiere comprar unos artículos. Esa página indica cómo pagar por lo que compra y cómo comunicarse con la compañía. También incluye información sobre garantías, descuentos y qué opciones tiene si no le gusta lo que compra.

3 Margarita selecciona dos jeans, tres camisetas de diferentes colores, dos pantalones cortos, un suéter negro, una sudadera morada, una chaqueta y unos zapatos. También compra el especial de la semana, una minifalda azul que cuesta sólo veinte pesos. ¡Perfecto!

4 Luego, Margarita tiene una pregunta: "¿Cómo puedo determinar si esta ropa y estos zapatos me van a quedar bien?" Decide consultar la página donde hay información para ayudar a los clientes a determinar esto.

5 Después, Margarita decide pagar por toda la ropa con su tarjeta de crédito, pero tiene otra pregunta: "¿Garantiza este sitio la protección de mi información personal?" Consulta otra página donde informan a los clientes que sí hay protección.

6 Cuando la ropa llega a su casa, Margarita está muy contenta. Toda la ropa que compró le queda bien y los colores son brillantes.

Answer questions 1–5. Base your answers on the reading *"Necesito comprar ropa."*

1 According to the article, why is Margarita concerned about ordering from an online catalog?

  A She's worried that she won't receive the items on time.
  B She's worried that her personal information might not be protected.
  C She's worried that she can't return the items if she's unhappy with them.
  D She's worried that the items might look different from the way they look in the catalog.

2 Which of the following things does Margarita do?

  F She decides to go to an Internet site to look for clothing that she needs.
  G She looks for clothes at the mall first and cannot find any that she likes.
  H She picks out jeans, jackets, sneakers, and a necklace.
  I She buys new clothes for school.

3 What is the main reason that Margarita shops online?

  A She does not have a car to go shopping.
  B She has always bought her clothes online.
  C She does not like to go to the mall.
  D All her friends shop online.

4 Which of the following is used by Margarita to pay for her purchases?

  F cash
  G check
  H layaway plan
  I credit card

5 If you were going to give someone advice on how to purchase clothing from the Internet, what would you say? Use details and information from the article to support your answer.

Nombre _____

Fecha _____

Answer Sheet

1 (A) (B) (C) (D)   **2** (F) (G) (H) (I)   **3** (A) (B) (C) (D)

4 (F) (G) (H) (I)

5

READ
THINK
EXPLAIN

_____

_____

_____

_____

_____

_____

_____

_____

Realidades **B**

Capítulo 8A

Nombre _____

Fecha _____

Actividad 12, p. 227

LA.A.2.3.8

Analyzing the Validity and Reliability of Information

When good readers analyze information for validity and reliability, one of the most important questions that they ask themselves about what they have read is "How do I know that I can trust that this information is true or accurate?" After answering this question, readers need to determine how such information can be used.

Tip

One way readers check information in a reading passage for validity and reliability is to ask, "How could I verify that this information is accurate or true?" Some ways to verify this include observing, taking measurements, conducting experiments, getting advice from experts in that particular field, and interviewing people with firsthand experience.

1. On page 227 of your textbook, review **Actividad 12 "¿Quieres aprender a bucear?"** Then read the statements below from this activity and explain how, if at all, you could verify their truth or accuracy.

   ¡Aprende a bucear en sólo tres cursos!

   _____

   _____

   Practica un deporte interesante y divertido.

   _____

   _____

   Pasa tiempo en un lugar fantástico.

   _____

   _____

   Hay un lenguaje especial que permite a los buzos comunicarse en el agua con señales.

   _____

   _____

   En los cursos de buceo, puedes aprender estas señales.

   _____

   _____

Sample FCAT question:

2. TIf you were using the brochure for *Escuela de buceo "Flor del mar"* for a research project about scuba diving in the Dominican Republic, which information seems least reliable?
   A Scuba diving is an interesting and fun sport.
   B You can learn hand signals in the diving courses, and this will help you as a diver.
   C You can learn to scuba dive after only three classes.
   D One of the most important hand signals for scuba divers is "Danger!"

Realidades **B**

Capítulo 8A

Nombre

Fecha

Lectura, pp. 240–241

LA.A.1.3.2

Strategies to Analyze Words: Context Clues

It is impossible to know the meaning of every word in a language. Good readers develop strategies to determine the meanings of unknown words as they read without having to look all of them up in the dictionary. Good readers examine the sentences surrounding new vocabulary words looking for context clues that might help them guess the meaning of the new word.

Tip

Good readers pay attention to the punctuation marks next to unusual vocabulary words because they know that writers will often place a comma after an unusual word and then describe or define that word in a parenthetical expression. This expression could be a one-word description, a descriptive phrase, or an even longer relative clause. Look at how this works with the unusual word, **vitamina:**

One-word description: We drank a *vitamina*, a smoothie, and it gave us energy.

Descriptive phrase: We drank a *vitamina*, a fruity milk shake with oatmeal and honey in it.

Relative clause: We drank a *vitamina*, which is a hearty drink consisting of yogurt, ice, bananas, strawberry, honey, and oatmeal.

Notice that when these parenthetical expressions are used in the middle of a sentence, a comma comes both before and after the expression. If the expression comes at the end of the sentence, a period will often follow the expression.

1. After reviewing the **Lectura** in your textbook on pages 240–241, *Álbum de mi viaje a Perú,* record the description or definition given in the **Lectura** for the terms listed below. For each term, tell if the parenthetical expression after it is an one-word description, descriptive phrase, or relative clause.

	Definition/Description	Type
Cuzco	_____	_____
Lima	_____	_____
Machu Picchu	_____	_____
Hiram Bingham	_____	_____

Sample FCAT question:

2. Read the sentence below and then choose the best meaning for the underlined word.

Viewed from above, *las líneas de Nazca* resemble the <u>hieroglyphics</u>, picture writing, of the ancient Egyptians.

A geometric figures
B a language system that uses symbols or drawings as words
C giant bird figures sketched in the sands of the Peruvian desert
D cave paintings found throughout North Africa and Europe

Spanish Missions in Texas

1   Since the earliest days of Spanish exploration in the Americas, a highly successful mission system was put in place. In the southeastern United States, it extended from Florida up to North Carolina, and in the southwest from Texas to California. Through this system, Catholic priests received financial and military support from the Spanish Crown to build missions where the priests could convert the indigenous people not only to the Catholic faith, but also to the Spanish way of life. The priests were protected by Spanish soldiers as new lands were claimed, although very often these two groups disagreed about the best way to treat the new converts. The priests were the protectors of the indigenous and taught them religion as well as valuable vocational skills.

San José Mission

2   In 1690, the first Spanish mission in Texas was founded: San Francisco de los Tejas. Several other missions were established shortly thereafter and in close proximity to each other. All were in East Texas, an area that was plagued by disease, drought, constant attacks from indigenous inhabitants who rejected the Spaniards' presence, and threats from the French who fought for power in the same region. For these reasons, the missions were closed and four were relocated along the San Antonio River in what is now the city of San Antonio. By 1731, there were five missions established around this area: San Antonio de Valero (1718), San José (1720), San Juan Capistrano (1731), Concepción (1731), and San Francisco de Espada (1731). The dirt road that linked all the missions was known as *El Camino Real*, a route that began in Mexico City and continued up through the northernmost territories of Nueva España, as Mexico was then called. Today these territories are the west and southwest regions of the United States.

3   The oldest and best known of these missions is San Antonio de Valero, named for the Spanish viceroy of Mexico, el marqués de Valero. It is also known as the Alamo, one of the most famous landmarks in Texas history. The original building was made of sticks and straw, but these flimsy

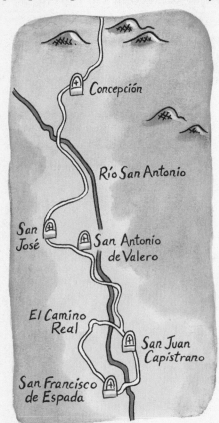

Concepción

Río San Antonio

San José

San Antonio de Valero

El Camino Real

San Juan Capistrano

San Francisco de Espada

Spanish Missions in Texas (*continued*)

building materials made it an easy victim of attacks. Subsequent construction of this and other missions was made with sturdier materials, such as sandstone, which could be cut into slabs for floors and walls, or certain clay soils, which were made into tiles and bricks. Although some of the missions were more elaborate than others, their overall architectural style was simple and practical.

4 The mission of San José was the best fortified and most successful and soon became an important social and cultural center. It was also considered the most beautiful. San José was founded by Fray Antonio Margil de Jesús, a Franciscan priest who was born in 1657 in Valencia, Spain. While still in his early teens, Margil expressed interest in becoming a Franciscan and at the age of twenty-five he was ordained. Soon thereafter, he was on his way to the New World as a missionary. After serving in Costa Rica, Guatemala, and Mexico, he went on to help establish missions in East Texas. These missions are considered the <u>cornerstone</u> from which other missions in Texas grew.

5 As protectors of the indigenous inhabitants, the Franciscans opened workshops in the missions in order to teach them trades. Under the priests' guidance, they learned such skills as carpentry and masonry in order to enhance the construction of the missions, as well as blacksmithing, which was needed to repair farm tools. The mission of San Juan Capistrano became a major supplier of agricultural products in the region, along with wood, iron, cloth, and leather goods that the indigenous inhabitants produced in the mission's workshops.

6 The mission of Concepción (full name: Misión Nuestra Señora de la Purísima Concepción de Acuna) is the best preserved of the San Antonio missions, with 45-inch thick walls. It has what many consider

to be the oldest fully preserved church building in the United States. Concepción was well-known for its religious celebrations.

7 The mission of Espada is unique because of its irrigation system, the oldest still in use in the United States. Missions depended on a steady harvesting of crops for the survival of their residents. Because rainfall was irregular in this part of Texas, an irrigation system was a top priority. Irrigation was so important that settlers measured the farmland in <u>*suertes*</u>, which is the amount of land that they could water in a day.

8 Today, the Alamo is a visitor's center and museum. The other four missions—San José, San Juan, Concepción, and Espada—are functioning Catholic parishes and are open to the public. All are popular tourist destinations.

San Francisco de Espada Mission

Answer questions 1–5. Base your answers on the reading *"Spanish Missions in Texas."*

1 In the following sentence, what does the word *suertes* mean?

Irrigation was so important that settlers measured the farmland in <u>suertes</u>, which is the amount of land that they could water in a day.

A a kind of farming system

B luck

C a kind of land measurement

D crops

2 Which of the following would be another good title for this passage?

F "Spanish Soldiers Conquer the Southeastern Part of the United States"

G "Catholic Priests and Spanish Soldiers"

H "Missions: A Popular Tourist Destination"

I "Building of the Spanish Missions System in the Southeastern and Southwestern United States"

3 Why were the missions closed in East Texas?

A Because the region was plagued by disease, drought, constant attacks from indigenous inhabitants, and threats from the French.

B Because the region was not fortified and easily destroyed.

C Because the missions were established in too close proximity.

D Because the missions ran out of farmland to grow crops.

4 What can you infer from the passage about the mission of San Juan Capistrano?

F The indigenous inhabitants did not accept the presence of the Franciscans.

G The indigenous inhabitants did not feel protected by the Franciscans.

H The indigenous inhabitants accepted the presence of the Franciscans.

I The Franciscans of this mission tried to destroy the indigenous inhabitants' village.

5 READ THINK EXPLAIN Compare and contrast the various Spanish missions. Support your answer with details and information from the article.

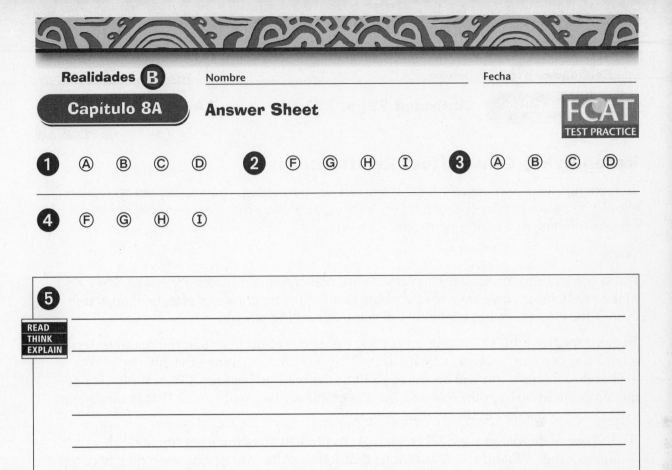

Realidades **B**

Capítulo 8A

Nombre _____

Fecha _____

Answer Sheet

FCAT **TEST PRACTICE**

1 Ⓐ Ⓑ Ⓒ Ⓓ   **2** Ⓕ Ⓖ Ⓗ Ⓘ   **3** Ⓐ Ⓑ Ⓒ Ⓓ

4 Ⓕ Ⓖ Ⓗ Ⓘ

5

READ
THINK
EXPLAIN

Recognizing Cause-Effect Relationships

To recognize cause-effect relationships in fiction, nonfiction, drama, or poetry, readers should be aware of why things happen (causes) as well as the consequences or results of actions (effects) in a reading passage.

Tip

Good readers can recognize when effects are presented in a reading passage. They also make predictions while they read and can predict the outcomes or effects of an action even if the effects are not explicitly written in a reading passage.

To gain practice with predicting outcomes, you should find places in the reading passage where you can stop and ask a "What if . . . ?" question. Sometimes the answer to your "What if . . . ?" question will be stated right in the reading passage. Other times, your question might be hypothetical and the acceptable answer will be one that makes sense, even if it is not stated in the reading passage.

1. In your textbook on page 271, review **Actividad 30 *"Las tortugas tinglar"*.** Then answer the "What if . . . ?" questions that follow. After answering each question, tell if the answer was in the reading passage or if you had to arrive at the answer logically.

   What if the tinglar turtle were not so big?

   _____
   _____
   _____

   What if the tinglar turtle were not in danger of extinction?

   _____
   _____
   _____

   What if volunteers from different countries did not go to the beaches of Culebra Island?

   _____
   _____
   _____

   What if, after hatching from eggs, tinglar turtles went immediately to swim in the ocean?

   _____
   _____
   _____

Sample FCAT question:

2. What effect have volunteers had on the population of tinglar turtles on Culebra Island?
   A Their camping on the beaches has destroyed vital habitat for the tinglar turtle.
   B They have taught the turtles how to lay and hatch eggs.
   C They have helped newly hatched turtles progress to life in the ocean.
   D Their patrols on the beaches have saved the turtles from hunters.

Realidades B

Capítulo 8B

Nombre _____

Fecha _____

Lectura, pp. 272–273

LA.A.2.3.2

Determining the Author's Purpose

To determine the author's purpose for writing a book, a story, an article, or any other text, the reader must figure out why the author wrote that particular book, story, article, or text. Some common purposes for writing are to inform, to entertain, to persuade, or to describe. Readers should also be able to explain why the author uses different techniques or includes different features within a text.

Tip

When presented with a multi-paragraph text, good readers will often "chunk" the text into different sections to improve their understanding. The chunk might be a paragraph itself. In longer texts, a chunk is more likely to include several paragraphs. When you chunk a text, you are able to identify both the main idea of that chunk and the author's purpose for including that chunk in the text.

1. On pages 272–273 in your textbook, re-read the **Lectura,** *Hábitat para la Humanidad Internacional.* Examine below how the text has been separated into six different chunks. Identify the main idea for each chunk and author's purpose for including that chunk in the text.

	Main Idea	Author's Purpose
1 "Hábitat es una..."		
2 "Guatemala tiene catorce..."		
3 "Ayer fue mi..."		
4 "La mayoría del..."		
5 ¿Sabes que el...?"		
6 "Es una experiencia..."		

Sample FCAT question:

2. What was the author's purpose in the fourth paragraph for including the quotation from a lady of the Baja Verapaz community?
   A to entertain readers with a humorous story about volunteers
   B to provide a real life example of a type of person mentioned in the previous paragraph
   C to provide background information for the subsequent paragraph that mentions former President Jimmy Carter
   D to explain how money for Habitat for Humanity is collected and spent

¡Bienvenidos *a la calle* Olvera!

1 Si vas a Los Ángeles, debes visitar la calle Olvera, que está en el centro viejo de la ciudad y que tiene una atmósfera totalmente mexicana. En el año 1930, esta calle se transformó en un mercado mexicano donde puedes comprar toda clase de productos mexicanos y comer platos mexicanos auténticos. Los fines de semana muchas personas comen en los restaurantes y los mariachis tocan música en la plaza cerca de esta calle.

2 La calle Olvera lleva el nombre de Agustín Olvera, quien vivió en una casa delante de la plaza en el <u>siglo</u> XIX y fue uno de los primeros oficiales de la ciudad. Esta calle es una de las más viejas de la ciudad y tiene mucho interés histórico. Allí están muchos de los lugares más viejos como Casa Pelanconi,

en donde está situado el Café La Golondrina, el primer restaurante en Los Ángeles de comida mexicana auténtica.

3 Si estás en la calle Olvera en un día de fiesta mexicana, puedes observar tradiciones y ceremonias muy importantes de la cultura mexicana. Algunos de los días de fiesta mexicana más populares se celebran en la plaza cerca de la calle Olvera. El Cinco de Mayo conmemora la victoria de los mexicanos sobre los franceses en Puebla en 1862. El 16 de septiembre se celebra el Día de la Independencia de México porque ése fue el día en 1810 en que los mexicanos declararon su independencia de España. El dos de noviembre se celebra el Día de los Muertos, el día en que las familias mexicanas van a los cementerios para conmemorar a sus familiares muertos. Cada noche del 16 al 24 de diciembre se celebran las posadas, una fiesta que

conmemora los nueve días cuando la Virgen María y San José buscaron un lugar para descansar con el Niño Jesús.

4 Hoy la calle Olvera forma parte del Monumento Histórico del Pueblo de Los Ángeles. Si la visitas, vas a tener una experiencia muy interesante. Casi dos millones de personas visitan la calle Olvera cada año para participar en las actividades culturales, comer en los restaurantes y aprender más sobre la historia de Los Ángeles.

Realidades B

Capítulo 8B

**LA.A.2.3.2, LA.A.2.3.1,
LA.A.1.3.2, LA.A.2.2.7**

FCAT
TEST PRACTICE

Answer questions 1–5. Base your answers on the reading *"¡Bienvenidos a la calle Olvera!"*

1 Which of the following statements best describes how the celebration of *las posadas* differs from the other celebrations mentioned?

A It takes place over a period of several days and commemorates a religious event.

B It commemorates a famous event in Mexican history.

C It commemorates a famous tradition celebrated in Mexico.

D It takes place only once a year.

2 In the following sentence, what does the word *siglo* mean?

La calle Olvera lleva el nombre de Agustín Olvera, quién vivió en una casa delante de la plaza en el <u>siglo</u> XIX y fue unos de los primeros oficiales de la ciudad.

F year

G period

H century

I time

3 What is the main idea of the reading passage?

A Olvera Street is a street in Los Angeles that offers a modern re-creation of a Mexican village.

B Olvera Street is a street in Mexico that offers various activities for tourists.

C Olvera Street is a street in Mexico where you can see many Mexican celebrations.

D Olvera Street is an old street in the old center of Los Angeles, where you can see the first authentic Mexican restaurant and observe important traditions and ceremonies on Mexican holidays.

4 Which of the following statements best describes weekends on Olvera Street?

F Many people eat at the Mexican restaurants and the mariachi bands play music in the plaza near the street.

G Many people attend services at the famous Catholic Church located on Olvera Street.

H Many people come to this street so they can cross the border into Mexico easily.

I Many people visit the old schoolhouse on Olvera Street.

5 Using the information and details from the article, why do you think *La Calle Olvera* is a historical monument?

FCAT
TEST PRACTICE

1 Ⓐ Ⓑ Ⓒ Ⓓ **2** Ⓕ Ⓖ Ⓗ Ⓘ **3** Ⓐ Ⓑ Ⓒ Ⓓ

4 Ⓕ Ⓖ Ⓗ Ⓘ

5

READ
THINK
EXPLAIN

_____

_____

_____

_____

_____

_____

_____

_____

Realidades B

Capítulo 9A

Nombre _____

Fecha _____

Actividad 12, p. 291

LA.A.2.3.2

Determining the Author's Point of View

To determine the author's point of view in a reading selection, the reader must figure out how the author feels about a subject in the reading selection. To begin with, you should be able to identify when an author feels positive, negative, or neutral toward a subject. As you gain more practice with this skill, you should be able to identify a wide range of emotions or attitudes shown by authors. Some of these emotions or attitudes might include admiration, nostalgia, sarcasm, surprise, and sympathy.

Tip

To figure out the author's point of view toward his or her subject, try to locate words, phrases, or sentences in which the author expresses an emotional reaction or an opinion. It helps to know how to distinguish facts from opinions.

1. Review **Actividad 12** on page 291 in your textbook. Pay special attention to the movie reviews *"En nuestra opinión."* Now examine the excerpts from the movie reviews listed below. Identify each as a fact or opinion. Describe what the opinions express about the author's feelings or attitude toward his or her subject.

	Fact or Opinion	Feelings Expressed by Opinions
"Esta película, de dos horas y media, es similar a las viejas fórmulas de las telenovelas..."	_____	_____
"Recomendable para personas que no tienen nada que hacer."	_____	_____
"Una producción... que combina elementos de comedia y ciencia ficción."	_____	_____
"Es tan fascinante y cómica que no puedes creer que estás en el cine por más de tres horas."	_____	_____

Sample FCAT question:

2. The movie critic's point of view toward the film *Mis padres son de otro planeta* could best be described as
   A disappointed with the movie's length.
   B cautious about recommending it for an audience of adults.
   C incredulous that anyone would pay money to see this film.
   D enthusiastic about the movie's content.

Realidades B

Capítulo 9A

Nombre _____

Fecha _____

Lectura, pp. 300–301

LA.A.2.3.1

Identifying Methods of Development and Patterns of Organization

Good readers understand the tools and techniques of authors. To identify the methods of development used by an author in a text, good readers must first determine the author's purpose by asking, "Why was this text written?" After determining the author's purpose, readers next ask, "What techniques did the author use to achieve his or her purpose?" These techniques are known as methods of development and could include, among other things, the organization pattern, the word choice, or the sentence structure used in the text.

Tip

One common pattern of organization for writers is the problem-solution essay. Readers can expect a problem-solution essay to address, but not be limited to such sub-topics as a description of the problem, its causes and effects, statistics about real-life examples, and possible solutions.

1. On pages 300–301 of your textbook, review the **Lectura,** *Una semana sin televisión.* Then look at the chart below and fill out information from the reading passage that relates to one of the sub-topics.

Sub-Topics About the Problem	Information from *"Una semana sin televisión"*
Description:	_____ _____ _____
Causes:	_____ _____ _____
Effects:	_____ _____ _____
Statistics:	_____ _____
Possible solutions:	_____ _____ _____

Sample FCAT question:

2. All of the following issues related to the problem of excessive television viewing are addressed in the reading passage *Una semana sin televisión* EXCEPT:

   A causes of the problem.

   B effects of the problem.

   C statistics about the problem.

   D possible solutions to the problem.

52 *FCAT Support* ━ *Capítulo 9A*

Spanish-Language Television in the United States

1 Spanish-language television was first broadcast in the United States in New York City and San Antonio in the mid-1940s, at approximately the same time as English-language television. The Spanish-language programs were shown in various time slots on certain English-language channels. The first full-fledged Spanish-language station, KCOR-TV in San Antonio, began broadcasting in 1955. Among its early shows was *Buscando estrellas,* a talent show that brought young entertainers from Mexico to Texas.

2 Today there is a large, well-established audience for Spanish-language broadcasting in the United States. Viewers can enjoy *telenovelas* and other entertainment shows from Mexico, Argentina, Venezuela, and Spain, as well as from such U.S. cities as New York and Miami. International sports events are beamed by satellite from around the globe, with commentary and play-by-play coverage in Spanish.

3 Because Hispanic populations in the United States represent many different countries and cultures, it has been a challenge to create programs that will appeal to this diverse market. One major success was a *telenovela* entitled *Angélica, mi vida,* produced in Puerto Rico in the 1980s. Its subplots dealt with love, tragedy, and power among families of Puerto Rican, Cuban, and Mexican origin.

4 Today's programs include the most-watched talk show in the world, Miami-based *Cristina,* and the longest-running show on Spanish-language television, *Sábado gigante,* which began broadcasting from Miami in 1986. Cuban-born Cristina Saralegui, who hosts her own show, engages her guests and audiences in lively debates on topical issues. *Sábado gigante* is hosted by Chilean-born Mario Kreutzberger, who uses the pseudonym Don Francisco on his show, which features

Cristina Saralegui

celebrity guests, contests, games, comedy, and interviews on topics of interest to the Hispanic community. Popular programs originating from outside the United States include *El show de Chespirito* (Mexico), *Informe semanal* (Spain), and *Sábados felices* (Colombia).

5 English-language shows dubbed into Spanish are also shown on Spanish-language TV channels. Among the longest-running of these are cartoon series, such as *The Pink Panther* (*La Pantera rosa*) and *Spiderman* (*El Hombre araña*).

Don Francisco

Answer questions 1–5. Base your answers on the reading *"Spanish-Language Television in the United States."*

1 Which statement best describes Spanish-language television in the United States?

A Spanish-language television programs reflect only the Spanish (from Spain) population in the United States.

B Spanish-language television reflects the various Hispanic populations in the United States.

C Spanish-language programs are always English-language shows dubbed into Spanish.

D Spanish-language programs have a small Mexican audience.

2 How did the various Hispanic populations have an effect on Spanish-language television?

F Spanish-language television programs were created to appeal to this diverse market from many Spanish-speaking countries.

G Spanish-language television programs were produced to appeal to Puerto Ricans.

H Spanish-language television programs were produced to appear more like English-language programs from the United States

I Spanish-language television programs were produced to appeal to Spanish audiences only.

3 How do the shows *Cristina* and *Sábado Gigante* differ?

A *Cristina* has a Cuban-born woman who hosts a show, while *Sábado Gigante* has a Chilean-born host.

B *Cristina* is produced in Cuba, while *Sábado Gigante* is produced in Chile.

C *Cristina* appeals to a Cuban-American audience while *Sábado Gigante* appeals to a Chilean-American audience.

D *Cristina* is a variety show that hosts celebrity guests, contests, comedy, and games, while *Sábado Gigante* engages its guests in lively debates.

4 What can you infer as the meaning of the word *telenovela*?

F a variety show with comedy

G a show engaging guests in lively debates

H a soap opera

I a news program

5 How would you support the idea that Spanish-language television has grown significantly since the mid-1940's? Support your answer using details and information from the article.

Nombre _____ Fecha _____

Answer Sheet

1 Ⓐ Ⓑ Ⓒ Ⓓ **2** Ⓕ Ⓖ Ⓗ Ⓘ **3** Ⓐ Ⓑ Ⓒ Ⓓ

4 Ⓕ Ⓖ Ⓗ Ⓘ

5

READ
THINK
EXPLAIN

_____

_____

_____

_____

_____

_____

_____

_____

Realidades B

Capítulo 9B

Nombre _____

Fecha _____

Actividad 8, p. 317

LA.A.2.4.8

Drawing Conclusions

To draw a conclusion is to form an opinion based on evidence. Sometimes the evidence presented to readers is very limited, but they must ensure that their evidence-based opinions make logical sense.

Conclusion statements are simply right or wrong. They are often presented as believable or not. If you are successful at drawing conclusions from your reading, then you likely are skilled at finding evidence in your reading that supports your conclusions.

Conclusions are only as strong as the evidence on which they are based. Conclusions based on little evidence are not as believable as conclusions based on a lot of different kinds of evidence. You must also be willing to change your conclusions as more evidence becomes available in the reading passage.

Tip

Readers must be flexible in their thinking if drawing conclusions from multiple and varied pieces of evidence. When the pieces of evidence are similar or the amount of evidence is limited, drawing conclusions is not difficult.

1. On page 317, review the quiz *"La computadora y tú"* in **Actividad 8.** Below you will find excerpts from the test questions that will serve as pieces of evidence. For each set of evidence, draw a conclusion that makes logical sense.

Easy
- Ana communicates most often with people by visiting chat rooms.
- When she writes reports, Ana most often finds information by downloading documents from the Internet.
- Ana knows how to design her own Web page.

Conclusion about Ana: _____

More difficult
- Henry goes to the library to get books when he needs information to write a report.
- Henry uses computers to play interactive games.
- Henry communicates most often with people by e-mail.
- Henry does not know how to write a composition using the computer.

Conclusion about Henry: _____

Sample FCAT question:

2. Which conclusion below is LEAST credible about a person who would choose letter A responses for all the questions on the test titled *"La computadora y tú"*?
   A Such a person might prefer human contact to interaction with a computer.
   B Such a person will need training to become comfortable using a computer.
   C Such a person will never acquire computer skills.
   D Such a person might not like working with computers.

Realidades **B**

Capítulo 9B

Nombre _____

Fecha _____

Lectura, pp. 328–329

LA.A.2.2.7

Recognizing the Use of Comparison and Contrast

To recognize comparison and contrast in a reading passage, good readers can point out how items or ideas in the reading passage are similar to or different from each other. Sometimes writers will directly state that they are comparing or contrasting items in a reading passage. Other times readers might recognize items in a reading passage that could be compared or contrasted even though the writer might not have presented the information for that purpose.

Tip

One common way that comparison and contrast appears in a reading passage is in the form of a debate. A debate usually involves an argument over a controversial issue. When you encounter a debate in a reading passage, you should identify the two sides of the issue, known commonly as the pro (in favor of) and the con (against) positions.

1. Review the **Lectura** *"La invasión del ciberspanglish"* on pages 328–329 in your textbook. Then fill in the blanks of the chart below.

   The issue debated in the **Lectura,** *La invasión del ciberspanglish* is

   _____

   _____ .

   **Arguments supporting
   the PRO position**

   _____

   _____

   _____

   _____

   _____

   **Arguments supporting
   the CON position**

   _____

   _____

   _____

   _____

   _____

Sample FCAT question:

2. Which is NOT a reason given to support the idea that it is acceptable to mix English and Spanish?
   A It makes communication easier.
   B Spanish is a language as rich as English.
   C Expressing technical terms in Spanish is too complicated.
   D If a computer word has an English origin, it makes little sense to translate it to Spanish.

Música latina *en la televisión*

¿Te gusta ver los videos musicales de Ricky Martin, Marc Anthony, Gloria Estefan, Jennifer Lopez y otros artistas latinos? Pues, la siguiente información te va a interesar.

1 *MTV Latino* es un canal de televisión por cable que empezó en 1993 y que da programas musicales las 24 horas del día. Es el canal favorito del 50 por ciento de los jóvenes latinos en los Estados Unidos. A ellos les fascina porque en este canal dan toda clase de videos musicales, noticias sobre música, artistas, bandas, conciertos y películas y entrevistas con los artistas más populares. También los jóvenes pueden llamar por teléfono y pedir su video favorito.

Ricky Martin canta y baila al ritmo latino.

Gloria Estefan canta con Justin Timberlake y JC Chasez de *NSync.

2 *MTV en Telemundo* también da programas musicales para los jóvenes. Este programa de televisión por cable, que empezó en septiembre de 1999, es una colaboración entre Telemundo, una de las compañías más grandes de programación en español, y MTV Latinoamérica. Los viernes a las once y media de la noche y los sábados a las once de la noche, los jóvenes pueden ver los diez videos musicales más populares de la semana y también los bailes más populares del mundo latino.

Realidades B

Capítulo 9B

LA.A.2.3.1, LA.A.2.2.7

Answer questions 1–5. Base your answers on the article *"Música latina en la televisión."*

1 How does *MTV en Telemundo* differ from *MTV Latino*?

  A It offers musical programming, but not on a 24-hour basis.
  B It is available on cable television.
  C It is older than *MTV Latino*.
  D It presents music videos.

2 According to the reading, which of the following is not one of the reasons why teens watch *MTV Latino*?

  F It offers a variety of musical programming.
  G It presents news about and interviews with their favorite recording artists.
  H It allows them to call in and request their favorite videos.
  I It does not cost anything to receive it.

3 What is the main idea of this article?

  A Both *MTV Latino* and *MTV en Telemundo* began in 1993.
  B Both *MTV Latino* and *MTV en Telemundo* offer music and music videos for teenagers.
  C On both *MTV Latino* and *MTV en Telemundo*, young people can telephone the station to request their favorite music video.
  D Gloria Estefan, Justin Timberlake, JC Chasez, and Ricky Martin are the favorite singers on the MTV stations.

4 On which program do young people watch the ten most popular music videos and dances of the Latin world for that particular week?

  F *MTV en Telemundo*
  G *MTV Latino*
  H The Gloria Estefan Show
  I Ricky and his Latin Rhythm Show

5 **READ THINK EXPLAIN** How are *MTV Latino* and *MTV en Telemundo* similar?

Nombre _____ Fecha _____

Answer Sheet

1 Ⓐ Ⓑ Ⓒ Ⓓ　**2** Ⓕ Ⓖ Ⓗ Ⓘ　**3** Ⓐ Ⓑ Ⓒ Ⓓ

4 Ⓕ Ⓖ Ⓗ Ⓘ

5

READ
THINK
EXPLAIN

_____

_____

_____

_____

_____

_____

_____

_____

ISBN 0-13-166039-X

90000

9 780131 660397